PROBLEMS IN
UNDERGRADUATE PHYSICS

VOLUME II
ELECTRICITY AND MAGNETISM

D1447889

PROBLEMS IN UNDERGRADUATE PHYSICS

VOLUME II
ELECTRICITY AND MAGNETISM

BY

S. P. STRELKOV, I. A. EL'TSIN, AND
S. E. KHAIKIN

TRANSLATED BY
D. E. BROWN

TRANSLATION EDITED BY
D. TER HAAR

PERGAMON PRESS
OXFORD · LONDON · EDINBURGH · NEW YORK
PARIS · FRANKFURT

Pergamon Press Ltd., Headington Hill Hall, Oxford
4 & 5 Fitzroy Square, London W. 1

Pergamon Press (Scotland) Ltd., 2 & 3 Teviot Place, Edinburgh 1

Pergamon Press Inc., 122 East 55th St., New York 22, N.Y.

Pergamon Press GmbH, Kaiserstrasse 75, Frankfurt-am-Main

First edition 1965

Library of Congress Catalog Card Number 64-25443

This translation corresponds to the Russian book
Сборник задач по общему курсу физики, часть I
(third edition) published by Nauka, Moscow, 1964,
and includes amendments and additions supplied by the
authors during the course of the translation.

CONTENTS

PREFACE

THIS set of four books of problems is based on a translation of a Russian collection which has been in use by students in physics at Moscow State University and the Moscow Physico-Technical Institute for a number of years. Where appropriate, answers and solutions to the problems are given in the second part of each volume.

During the course of the translation of these volumes, the authors provided a large list of amendments and additions to their Russian text and these have all been incorporated in this English edition. Many of the additional problems are on topics which have developed during recent years.

The standard of the problems is roughly equivalent to an undergraduate course in physics at a British university or at an American university; it varies from the simple to the rather sophisticated. They can be used in conjunction with almost any textbook on physics at the appropriate level.

D. TER HAAR

PROBLEMS

PROBLEMS

§ 1. ELECTROSTATICS

1. To gain an idea of the size of a 1 Coulomb electric charge, calculate the force F of repulsion of two like charges each of 1 Coulomb at 1 km apart.

2. What is the force F of attraction of the electron of a hydrogen atom on the nucleus, if the atom diameter is of the order 2×10^{-8} cm? The charge on the nucleus is $4 \cdot 8 \times 10^{-10}$ e.s.u.

3. Two equal spheres of radius $r = 1$ cm and mass $m = 9 \cdot 81$ g are suspended by silk threads of length $l = 19$ cm from the same point. The spheres are given charges of the same magnitude and sign. What is the charge q_1 of each sphere if they separate so that the angle between the threads is $2\alpha = 90°$?

4. Will a point charge have a position of stable equilibrium when it is at the mid-point between two other equal point charges, the signs of which are either the same or opposite to that of the first charge?

5. Four equal charges e of the same sign are placed at the vertices of a square of side a. What charge e_1 of opposite sign must be placed at the centre of the square in order for the resultant of the forces acting on each charge to be zero?

6. Three equal charges e of the same sign are located at the vertices of an equilateral triangle. What charge e_1 of opposite sign must be placed at the centre of the triangle in order for the resultant of the forces acting on each charge to be zero?

7. Show that the charges of each sign induced on a conductor A when it is approached by a charge $+e$ (Fig. 1) is always less than e.

8. Find the field strength E inside and outside an infinite plane layer of thickness d, in which positive charge is uniformly distributed with density ϱ.

3

Hint. Use the symmetry of the system of charges and apply Gauss' theorem.

9. Electric charge is uniformly distributed with surface density $\sigma = 10$ e.s.u. on a vertical plate of large dimensions. A small sphere of mass $m = 1$ g carrying a charge of the same sign as the plate is suspended from a thread clamped to the plate. Find its charge e if the thread forms an angle $\varphi = 30°$ to the vertical.

10. Two long thin conductors are parallel to each other at a distance d apart, and are charged uniformly with charges of opposite sign with linear density $+\sigma$ and $-\sigma$. Find the field strength E at a point lying in the plane of symmetry at a distance x from the plane in which the conductors lie.

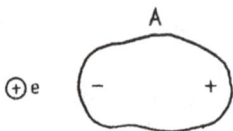

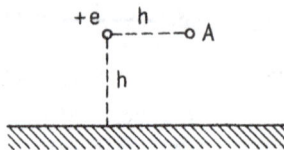

FIG. 1   FIG. 2

Hint. Use Gauss' theorem to find the field-strength produced by each conductor, then find the geometrical sum of these fields.

11. A disc of radius R is charged uniformly with surface density σ. Find the field-strength E at a point on the perpendicular through the centre of the disc, at a distance h from the disc.

12. Show that the force of interaction between a charge $+e$ and an infinite conducting plane at a distance d from the charge is the same as between the same charge $+e$ and a charge $-e$, located symmetrically relative to the plate.

13. A point charge $+e$ is at a distance h from an infinite conducting plane. Find the field-strength E at the point A (Fig. 2), which is at a distance h from the charge and the plane.

14. An infinite plane is uniformly positively charged with surface density σ. Find the potential difference V between a point A at a distance d from the plane and a point B on the plane.

15. Plot the lines of force and equipotential surfaces of a system of two point charges $+e$ and $+4e$, at a distance d apart.

Hint. Find the point at which the field-strength is zero. Find the points on the straight line joining the charges at which the potential is the same as at the point at which the field-strength is zero.

16. Two point charges of opposite sign, with magnitudes in the ratio n, are at a distance d apart. Show that the surface of zero potential is spherical, and find the radius R of this sphere and the distance x_0 of its centre from the lesser charge.

17. Show that, for two conductors as described in problem 10, and sufficiently remote from each other, i.e. $d \gg r$, where r is the radius of a conductor: (1) the equipotential surfaces are circular cylinders, the axes of which are parallel to the conductors and lie in the same plane; (2) the lines of force lie in a plane perpendicular to the conductors, and represent circles whose centres lie on the perpendicular through the mid-point of the segment joining the projections of the conductors.

18. Draw the lines of force and equipotential surfaces for a system of two point charges $+e$ and $-4e$.
Hint. Find the point at which the field-strength is zero. Find the sphere of zero potential, and also the point on the straight line joining the charges at which the potential is the same as at the point where the field-strength is zero.

19. A metal sphere of radius R is earthed via a very thin conductor. An electric charge $+e$ is situated at a distance $d = 2R$ from the centre of the sphere. What is the negative charge e' on the sphere? The surface of the earth and all other objects can be assumed sufficiently remote, and the effect of the earthing wire can be neglected.

20. Find the potential of the field produced by the charge uniformly distributed along an infinite straight line with linear density σ.

21. A long straight cylindrical conductor of radius r carries positive charge with uniform surface density σ. What is the potential difference V between the surface of the cylinder and a point A at a distance $d > r$ from the cylinder axis?

22. Given that the potential of the field in a certain region is $\varphi = -\frac{1}{2}ax^2 + c$, i.e. depends on the x coordinate only, what is the field-strength? What charge distribution will produce such a field?

23. Taking the earth as a sphere of radius 6400 km, find the charge e on the earth if the electric field-strength on the earth's surface is 130 V/m. Find the potential φ of the earth's surface.

24. A very small sphere carrying charge $+e$ is brought up to a small distance h from a large metallic sheet. What is the field-strength E: (1) at the base of the perpendicular from the sphere to the plane of the sheet; (2) at a distance $2h$ from the plane along this perpendicular?

25. Two like positive charges e are at the same distance d from an infinite conducting plane and on the same side of it. The distance between the charges is $2d$. Find the magnitude and direction of the field-strength vector at the mid-point between the charges.

26. A charged conductor lies inside a closed metallic sheath. (1) Does the electric field inside the sheath vary if a charged conductor is brought up from the outside? (2) Is there any change in the field inside and outside the sheath if the inner conductor is displaced inside the sheath?

27. What would be the field-strength E at the centre of a spherical surface of radius R if half this surface were covered by charge with constant density σ, and the other half were also covered with charge of twice the density?

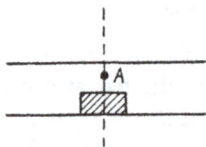

FIG. 3

28. A metallic sphere carries a certain charge. If the sphere is enclosed in a concentric spherical sheath of uniform dielectric, dielectric constant ε, what is the change in the electric field-strength inside and outside the sheath?

29. What answer can be given to the previous problem if the outer surface of the sheath is of arbitrary, instead of spherical, shape?

30. A dielectric plate is brought between two parallel conducting sheets, charged by equal charges of opposite sign, as illustrated in Fig. 3. Does the field-strength at the point A change when the plate is introduced?

31. What is the greatest charge Q that can be placed in a metallic sphere of radius $R = 15$ cm if the dielectric strength E of air can be taken as 30,000 V/cm?

32. A charge Q is uniformly distributed over a sphere of radius R. Find the pressure on the inner surface of the sphere due to interaction of the charges.

33. The pressure produced by the surface tension of a spherical liquid film is known to be inversely proportional to its radius.
Will a soap-bubble be stable if it is given a charge?

34. Charge is distributed uniformly with density σ over a spherical surface of radius R. Find the potential φ and field-strength E of the charge as a function of the distance d from the centre of the sphere. Draw graphs of these quantities.

35. A metal sphere of radius R_1, carrying charge Q, is surrounded by a concentric hollow metal sphere of inner radius R_2 and outer radius R_3. The charge on the outer sphere is zero. Draw a graph of the field-strength as a function of R. Find the potentials of the spheres if the potential at infinity is zero. Do the potentials of the spheres change if the outer one is earthed?

36. Draw graphs of the field-strength and potential as functions of the distance from the centre of a sphere in the following case: a metal sphere of radius 10 cm has a charge 20 e.s.u. and is surrounded by dielectric, of dielectric constant 2, the outer boundary of which is a sphere of radius 20 cm.

37. Two conductors have charges $-e$ and $+2e$ respectively. The conductors are carried inside a closed metallic sheath, the potential of which is V. Show that the potential of the conductor carrying the charge $+2e$ is greater than V.

38. A soap bubble, radius R, is in equilibrium. If a charge is communicated to it, it swells as a result of interaction between the charges and tends to take up a new stable state with radius $R_1 > R$ (see Problem 33). What charge must be located at the centre of the bubble in order to balance the action of these forces and maintain it at its original radius?

39. What field would be produced by two infinite perpendicular planes if they were charged uniformly with charge of the same sign, the surface densities of the charges being σ and 2σ respectively?

40. Given the conditions of the previous problem, find the equipotential surfaces and the law of variation of the potential on the planes carrying the charges.

41. Charges are distributed uniformly over the surfaces of two concentric spheres, radii 10 cm and 20 cm, the charge density being the same on both spheres. Find the charge density σ if the potential is 300 V at the centre, and zero at infinity.

42. Two concentric conducting spheres, radii R and $2R$, are charged: the inner by one microcoulomb, and the outer by two microcoulombs of electricity of the same sign. The potential $\varphi = 30$ e.s.u. at a distance $3R$ from the centre of the spheres. Find R.

43. What would be the field distribution in the space between the planes of Problem 39 if, in addition to the charges on the planes, a cylinder of radius R, whose axis coincides with the line of intersection of the planes, is given a surface charge -3σ?

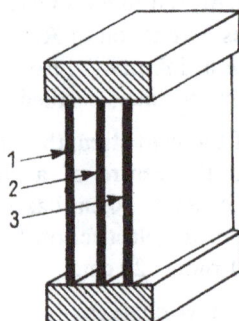

Fig. 4

44. What is the field-strength at an arbitrary point of space if charges are uniformly distributed with density σ on an infinite plane and on the surface of a sphere of radius R with its centre on the plane.

45. Calculate the mean density ϱ of the electric charges in the atmosphere in the following conditions: the electric field-strength on the earth's surface is known to be 100 V/m, whilst it drops to 25 V/m at a height $h = 1 \cdot 5$ km.

46. Three well-insulated parallel metal plates are mounted at an equal distance from one another, as shown in Fig. 4. Plate 1 is earthed; plates 1 and 3 are connected to the terminals of an 80 V battery. The battery is disconnected then plate 1 is disconnected from earth, whilst plate 2 is joined to earth. (1) What will be the potential difference between plates 1 and 2, and between 2 and 3? (2) What are the potential differences between the plates if, after disconnecting the battery, plate 2 is first joined to earth, then plate 1 disconnected from earth, and finally, plate 2 disconnected?

47. The 80 V battery is connected to plates 1 and 2 (see the previous problem) whilst plates 2 and 3 are shorted together. What are the potential differences between the pairs of plates if the battery is first disconnected, then the connection broken between plates 2 and 3, and finally, plate 3 connected to plate 1 (plate 2 is earthed throughout)?

48. Given the potentials V_1, V_2, V_3, V_4 at four neighbouring points situated at adjacent vertices of a cube, how can the field-strength in the neighbourhood of the points be found approximately?

49. Three identical plates are arranged parallel to each other at a distance 1 mm apart (this distance is very small compared with the plate dimensions). What are the potential differences between the plates if charge is distributed uniformly with density $+0\cdot2$ e.s.u. on the first, $+0\cdot4$ e.s.u. on the second and $-0\cdot6$ e.s.u. on the third?

50. What is the change in the potential differences between the plates of the previous problem if the space between them is filled with a dielectric with dielectric constant $\varepsilon = 2$?

51. Two infinitely long coaxial cylinders, radii $R_1 = 10$ mm and $R_2 = 10\cdot5$ mm, are charged to the same sign, the charge density on the outer cylinder being 2 e.s.u., and on the inner 1 e.s.u. Find the potential difference V between the cylinders.

52. Given the conditions of the previous problem, find the electric field-strength E outside the cylinders.

53. A freely rotating dipole with electric moment μ is situated in the field of a point charge e at a distance R away. How much work A must be done in order to remove the dipole to infinity? Assume that the length of the dipole is very small compared with R.

54. Is it possible for an electrostatic field to exist in a vacuum, such that the field-strength vector E has the same direction throughout the space, whilst it varies in magnitude say in accordance with a linear law, on passing from one point to another along the normal to the direction of the field (Fig. 5)?

55. An insulated conductor is charged to a certain positive potential. How does the conductor potential vary when an earthed conducting plane is brought up to a finite distance?

56. What change takes place in the potential between two insulated charged conductors when a metal plate, whose thickness cannot be neglected compared with the distance between the conductors, is brought between them?

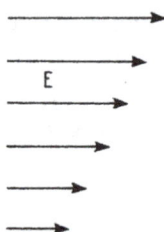

FIG. 5

57. Two identical metal plates of area S are remote from other bodies and are situated at a distance d, which is very small compared with the plate dimensions, from one another. One carries a charge $+e$, the other $+2e$. What is the potential difference between the plates?

58. Given the conditions of the previous problem, what is the nature of the electric field in the space between and outside the plates? What is the field-strength on the outer sides of the plates close to their mid-points?

59. Two conducting concentric spheres have radii $R_1 = 10$ cm, $R_2 = 20$ cm. Charge $Q = +50$ e.s.u. is distributed uniformly on each of them. What is the potential difference V between them and the field-strength inside and outside the spheres?

60. One coulomb of charge is communicated to a metal sphere of diameter 20 m. (1) What is the potential of the sphere relative to an infinitely remote concentric sphere? (2) Is the charge on the sphere retained if it is surrounded by air, the dielectric strength of which is 3 kV/mm?

61. Two identical circular discs of radius R, carrying charges of opposite signs, distributed uniformly with surface density σ, are at a small distance d from each other. Find the field-strength at the point A on their common axis, at a distance h from the nearer disc (Fig. 6).

62. The plates of a plane condenser are made of rectangular strips of foil measuring 5×10 cm², stuck on to insulated paper ($\varepsilon = 2$) of thickness 0·1 mm. A potential difference of 100 V is applied to the condenser. What is the charge Q (in electrostatic units) on each plate?

63. How does the field-strength change between the plates of an isolated plane condenser if the charge on one of the plates is doubled?

64. A plane condenser has a capacity of 600 pF. How does the capacity vary when copper foil, whose thickness is $\frac{1}{4}$ the distance between the plates, is placed parallel to and in between the plates? Is the result affected by the position of the foil?

65. A metal sphere, radius 5 cm, is surrounded by a spherical layer of dielectric ($\varepsilon = 7$) 1 cm thick and enclosed in a metal sphere with internal radius 7 cm, concentric with the first sphere. What is the capacity C of this condenser?

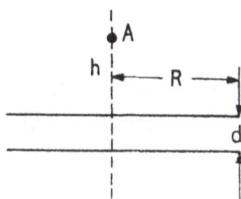

FIG. 6

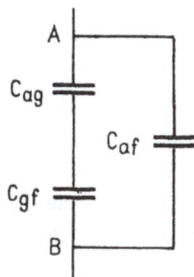

FIG. 7

66. Find approximately the capacity between two identical spheres of radius r, at a very large distance (compared with r) from one another. All other bodies are remote from the spheres.

67. The electrodes — anode, grid and cathode — of a thermionic valve have certain capacities relative to one another. It is convenient to consider them for design purposes, as small capacity condensers connected as shown in Fig. 7. If we write C_{ag} for the anode-grid capacity, C_{gf} for the grid-cathode capacity, and C_{af} for the anode–cathode capacity, what is the capacity C between the points A, B?

68. The procedure for measuring the capacities between the electrodes of a triode is as follows: the grid and anode are shorted together and the capacity C_1 measured between them and the cathode; then the cathode and anode are shorted and the capacity C_2 measured between these and the grid; finally, the grid and cathode are shorted together, and the capacity C_3 measured between these and the anode. How are the interelectrode capacities C_{af}, C_{ag} and C_{gf} determined from the measurements of C_1, C_2, C_3 (Fig. 7)?

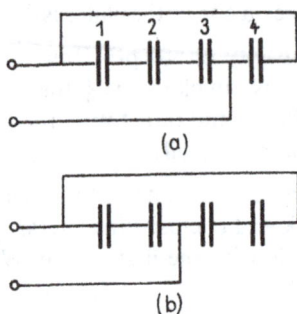

(a)

(b)

FIG. 8

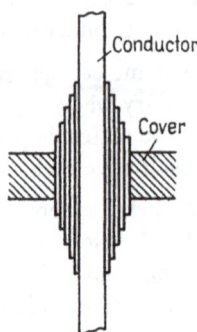

FIG. 9

69. A set of four identical condensers is first connected as shown in circuit (a), then as in circuit (b) (Fig. 8). (1) In which case is the capacity of the set the greater? (2) If the capacities of the condensers are different, what relationships must they satisfy in order for the capacity of the set to remain unchanged on switching from circuit (a) to (b)?

70. Show that the formulae for the capacities of cylindrical and spherical condensers transform to the formula for the capacity of a plane condenser when the difference between the radii of the inner and outer plates is small.

71. In high voltage transformers so-called condenser bushings are used for carrying the conductor through the cover. They consist of thin coaxial cylindrical insulating tubes, separated from one another by thin sheets of tin foil, and forming a combination of series-connected cylindrical condensers (Fig. 9). What is the length variation in the insulating tubes in order for all these condensers to have the same capacity? What is the purpose of such bushings?

72. A plane condenser consists of two plates 0·5 mm apart. What is the change in its capacity if it is placed in an insulated metal sheath ("screened"), the walls of which are 0·25 mm from the plates (Fig. 10)? Neglect the distortion of the field at the edges of the condensers.

FIG. 10

73. What is the change in the capacity of the sheathed condenser (see the previous problem) if the sheath is connected to one of the plates?

74. Two condensers, capacities C_1, C_2, are connected in series and joined to a source of constant voltage, V volts. Find the voltage drop in each condenser.

75. Four identical condensers are connected as shown in Fig. 11, and joined to a battery E. Switch II is open to start with, and switch I closed. Switch I is then opened and switch II closed. What will be the potential difference across each condenser if the e.m.f. of the battery E is 9 V?

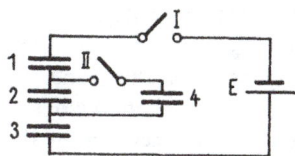

FIG. 11

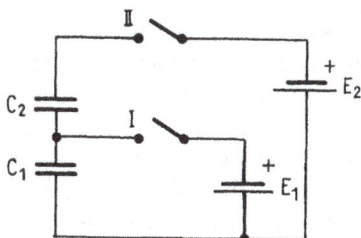

FIG. 12

76. Solve the previous problem on the assumption that switch I is closed, and is then opened when switch II is closed.

77. The two condensers C_1, C_2, illustrated in Fig. 12, are charged as follows. Switch I is first closed then opened, then switch II closed. Find the potential differences V_1, V_2 across the condensers if the battery e.m.f.'s are E_1, E_2.

78. The angle of opening of the leaves of an electroscope has a well-known dependence on the potential of a conductor to which the electroscope is joined. What condition must be satisfied by the capacity of the electroscope in order for a more exact measurement of the potential to be possible?

79. Two parallel plates of negligible thickness are charged simultaneously, the charge density on one plate being $\sigma_1 = +1$ e.s.u., and on the other $\sigma_2 = +2$ e.s.u. The distance D between the plates is 1 cm, which is small compared with the linear dimensions of the plates. A plane paraffin sheet, thickness $d = 5$ mm (Fig. 13), is inserted with its faces parallel to the plates. The dielectric constant of paraffin is $\varepsilon = 2$. Find the potential difference V (in volts) between the plates.

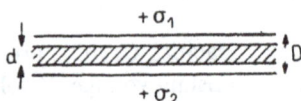

FIG. 13

80. Given the conditions of the previous problem, find: (1) the field-strength E_1 between the plates outside the dielectric; (2) the field-strength E_2 inside the dielectric; (3) the force F acting per 1 cm^2 of plate.

81. The charge on an electrified conductor can be measured by using an electrometer, which indicates potential differences. To start with, the potential difference V_1 between the conductor and earth is measured. Then a known capacity C_0 is joined to the conductor, the other terminal of the capacity being earthed, and the new potential difference V_2 is measured. How is the charge determined from these measurements? What does the accuracy of the determination depend on?

82. An air-spaced cylindrical condenser consists of a conductor, diameter 5 mm, and a coaxial cylinder, diameter 5 cm. To what potential difference V can the condenser be charged, if the dielectric strength of air is 30 kV/cm in the given conditions?

83. The distance between the plates of a plane condenser is d, and it is filled by two layers of dielectric. The thickness of the first layer, dielectric constant ε_1, is d_1. The dielectric constant of the second layer is ε_2. The area of each coating is S. Find the capacity C of the condenser.

84. The space between the plates of a plane condenser, distance d apart, is filled with dielectric. Find the capacity C of the condenser in two cases: (1) the dielectric consists of two layers of the same thickness, but with different dielectric constants ε_1, ε_2, the layers being parallel to the condenser plates; (2) half the condenser is filled by one dielectric, and half by another, in such a way that the boundary between the dielectrics is perpendicular to the plates. Neglect the field distortion at the dividing boundary. The plate area is S. Show that the capacity is always less in the first case than in the second.

85. The space between the plates of a plane condenser, plate area S, is filled with layered dielectric, consisting of n layers of material with dielectric constant ε_1 and n layers of material with dielectric constant ε_2. The layers alternate and each has a thickness d. Find the capacity C of the condenser.

86. The space between the plates of a plane condenser is filled with dielectric, the constant of which varies linearly from the value ε_1 at one plate to the value $\varepsilon_2 < \varepsilon_1$ at the other. The distance between the plates is d and the area of each is S. Find the capacity C of the condenser.

87. A battery maintaining a constant potential difference V is connected to the plates of a plane condenser, distance d apart. Dielectric is introduced into the condenser so as to fill the space between the plates. The dielectric constant is ε. What is the change in the electric charge density on the plates?

88. What is the field-strength E in the air-gap of a plane condenser if the potential difference between the plates is $V = 200$ V? The distance between the plates $D = 0\cdot2$ cm and there is a sheet of glass ($\varepsilon = 7$), thickness $d = 0\cdot1$ cm, between them.

89. A spherical condenser is half filled by dielectric of constant $\varepsilon = 7$. The surface radii are: $r = 5$ cm (inner), $R = 6$ cm (outer) (Fig. 14). Find the capacity C of the condenser, neglecting the distortion of the lines of force at the boundary of the dielectric.

90. Find the field between the plates of a spherical condenser, if the radius of the inner sphere is 5 cm, and of the outer 7 cm; the space between the spheres is filled with dielectric with $\varepsilon = 5$; the inner sphere carries a charge of 5000 e.s.u.

91. A uniform field of strength E exists in a dielectric medium of constant ε. The medium contains a spherical cavity. Find the field-strength E' at the centre of the sphere, produced by the charges induced on the surface of the sphere, assuming that the polarisation vector P is constant everywhere (except in the cavity).

Hint. The surface density of the induced charge on the boundary of the dielectric is equal to the magnitude of the polarisation vector P, multiplied by $\cos \theta$, where θ is the angle between the normal to the surface and the vector P (Fig. 15). Express the field-strength at the centre of the medium, produced by the inducted charge on an element of the spherical surface, and integrate over the medium.

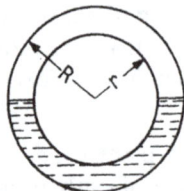
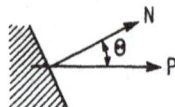

FIG. 14   FIG. 15

92. Show that the capacity between two concentric spherical surfaces, remote from the surface of the earth and other conductors, can be expressed by $C = R_2^2/(R_2 - R_1)$ when the inner sphere is earthed, where R_2, R_1 are respectively the radii of the outer and inner spheres.

93. A cylindrical condenser, in which the radius of one plate is twice that of the other, is charged to a potential difference V. Find the electric field-strength E at a point a distance d from the cylinder axis.

94. A condenser is joined to a source of constant voltage (battery). Does the field-strength in the condenser change if it is filled with dielectric?

95. There is a uniform flux of electrons in the space between the plates of a plane condenser, producing a uniform space charge. The distance between the plates is d. The potential of one of the plates is V_0. For what value of the density ϱ of the space charge are the potential and field-strength at the other plate zero?

96. The inner plate of a cylindrical condenser has radius R_2 and potential V_0. The outer plate, radius R_1, is earthed. A space charge of constant density ϱ exists between the plates. Find the distribution of the potential V between the plates.

97. A sheet of dielectric is displaced in the space between the plates of a plane condenser parallel to the plates. What forces act on that part of the sheet, in the neighbourhood of which the field can be assumed uniform?

98. The plates of a plane condenser carry charges $+Q$ and $-Q$. The plate area is S. What work A is done by the plates when they are brought together, from a distance d_0 to a distance d? What sort of energy is used for this work?

99. The plates of a plane condenser are connected to a battery. It is necessary to do work to move the plates apart. How does the required power vary with the distance, if the plates move apart uniformly? What is the work, performed when moving the plates apart, expended on? What happens to the initial electrostatic energy of the condenser?

100. A plane air-spaced condenser is charged to a potential difference V and disconnected from the source of e.m.f. The plate area is S, the distance between the plates is d. The plates are mounted vertically. A vessel containing liquid dielectric, constant ε, is brought up from below so that the dielectric fills half the condenser. (1) What is the capacity C of the condenser? (2) What is the field-strength E in the air-space and in the dielectric-filled space? (3) What is the distribution of the charge density σ over a plate? (4) Find the energy reduction ΔW of the condenser and say what this has been expended on. Assume that the liquid–air boundary is plane and that all the quantities change by a jump.

101. The interior of a plane condenser, total plate area 200 cm^2 and plate separation 0·1 cm, contains a sheet of glass ($\varepsilon = 5$) which fills it entirely. What change is there in the energy of the condenser if the glass sheet is removed? Solve the problem in two cases: (1) the condenser always remains joined to a battery of e.m.f. 300 V; (2) the condenser was originally connected to this battery but was disconnected prior to removing the glass. Find the mechanical energy consumed in removing the glass in each case.

102. The moving vanes of a variable condenser are at the central position. What moment M acts (due to the charge interaction) on the system of moving vanes with potential difference $V = 300$ V, if the number of "operative" spacings between the plates is $n = 20$,* each vane is in the form of a semi-circle, radius $r = 8$ cm, and the distance between two vanes is $d = 0.5$ mm?

103. A quartz plate is stretched by a force $P = 0.1$ kg. The side surfaces, perpendicular to the electrical axis, carry casings A and B of width $a = 3$ cm (Fig. 16), where the casing thickness $d \ll a$. The

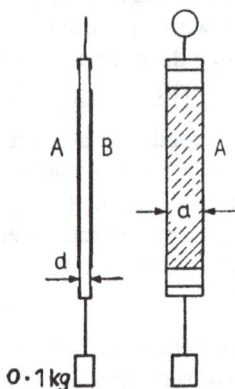

Fig. 16

casings are joined to an electrometer, the capacity of which is small compared with the capacity of the plane condenser formed by A and B. The electrometer shows that, when the loading P acts, the casings A, B acquire a potential difference $V = 1.8$ V. The dielectric constant of quartz is $\varepsilon = 4.5$. Find the piezo-electric constant α of quartz.

§ 2. DIRECT CURRENT LAWS

104. What is the resistance R of a piece of copper wire, diameter 2 mm, if the piece weighs 0.893 kg? The specific resistance of copper is 0.017×10^{-4} ohm cm and its specific weight is 8.93 g cm^{-3}.

105. The incandescent electric lamps invented by A. N. Lodygin (1872) used a small carbon rod. Calculate the wattage of Lody-

* There are 11 fixed vanes and 10 moving vanes.

gin's six-volt bulb if the length of the carbon rod was 6 cm and its diameter 2 mm. The specific resistance of carbon at 0°C is ϱ = 7×10^{-3} ohm cm and its temperature coefficient

$$\alpha = -2 \times 10^{-4} \text{deg}^{-1}.$$

The normal temperature of incandescence of the rod is 1600°C.

106. The base of an incandescent lamp with a tungsten filament is marked 120 V, 60 W. Measurement on a Wheatstone bridge of the resistance of the lamp when cold gave 20 ohm. What is the normal temperature of incandescence of the filament, if the temperature coefficient of the resistance of tungsten is $\alpha = 5 \times 10^{-3} \text{deg}^{-1}$?

107. The resistance of a 120 V, 100 W electric lamp is 10 times more when the lamp is hot than when it is cold. Find its resistance R when cold and the temperature coefficient, if the temperature of incandescence of the filament is 2000°C.

108. What diameter d must be chosen for a copper wire, in order for the voltage drop over a length of 1·4 km to be 1 V at a current of 1 amp?

109. When Lenz conducted the experiments in which he first accurately established the law for the amount of heat produced by a current (the Joule–Lenz law), he used a vessel filled with alcohol, in which was immersed a platinum spiral. He determined the amount of heat produced by a current by passing current through the spiral and measuring the time required for the temperature of the alcohol to rise 1°. Find the rate of temperature rise in Lenz's apparatus, if the wire of the platinum spiral had a length $l = 40$ cm and a diameter $d = 1$ mm; the voltage applied to the spiral $V = 1·1$ V, and the mass of the alcohol in the vessel $M = 1$ kg. The specific resistance of platinum at the operating temperature is $\varrho = 0·12 \times 10^{-4}$ ohm cm, the specific heat of alcohol is $c = 0·6$ cal g^{-1}deg^{-1}. Neglect the specific heat of the vessel and the heat losses.

110. An electrical circuit is formed from three pieces of wire of the same length and made of the same material, joined in series. The three pieces have different cross-sections: 1 mm², 2 mm², 3 mm². The potential difference across the ends of the circuit is 12 V. Find the voltage drop V in each piece of wire.

111. A circuit is formed from nine wires, forming a hexagon together with the diagonals issuing from the same vertex (Fig. 17).

The resistance of each of the wires is r. Determine the resistance R of the total circuit between the points A and B.

112. In the circuit illustrated in Fig. 18, r is a variable resistance. Draw the graph of the current as a function of the resistance r. The magnitudes E and R are known. Neglect the internal resistance of the battery.

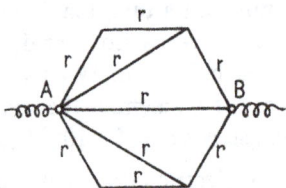

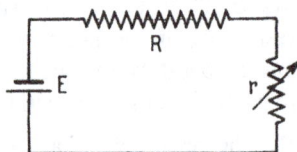

FIG. 17   FIG. 18

113. A battery of galvanic cells of e.m.f. E and internal resistance ϱ is connected across an external resistance R. Draw the graph of the variation of the voltage V over the external load as a function of R.

114. A battery is connected to a resistance $R_1 = 10$ ohm and produces a current $I_1 = 3$ amp. If the same battery is connected to a resistance $R_2 = 20$ ohm, the current becomes $I_2 = 1\cdot6$ amp. Find the e.m.f. E and the internal resistance r of the battery.

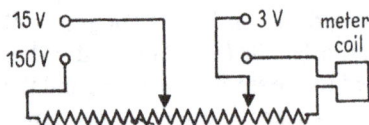

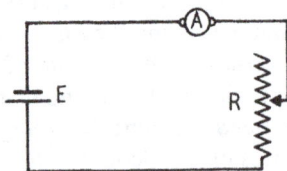

FIG. 19   FIG. 20

115. The circuit of a voltmeter is illustrated in Fig. 19; its scale has 150 divisions. It is equipped with four terminals, for measuring voltages up to 3, 15 and 150 V. When 1 mamp passes through the meter coil the needle moves over 50 divisions. What are the internal resistances of the voltmeter on the various ranges?

116. The size of a variable resistance R was determined by putting it in circuit with a battery of e.m.f. E and internal resistance ϱ and an ammeter of internal resistance R_{in} (Fig. 20). Estimate the accuracy of the measurement of R, i.e. establish the connection between the error ΔI of the current measurement and the error ΔR in determining the resistance, if the scale divisions of the meter are proportional to the current I.

117. The circuit of an ohmmeter for approximate resistance measurements is illustrated in Fig. 21. The meter element A has a resistance $\varrho = 2\cdot5$ kohm, and a scale of 100 divisions with a multiplying factor of $0\cdot5\,\mu$amp. The resistances shown in the diagram have the following values: $r_1 = 1$ ohm, $r_2 = 24$ ohm, $r_0 = 20$ kohm. The internal resistance of the battery is negligibly small.

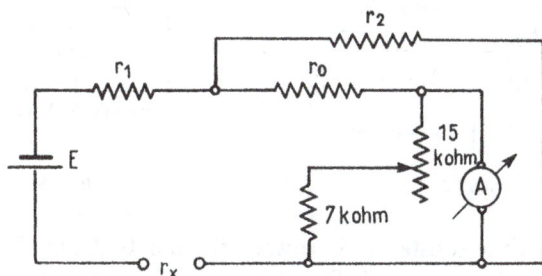

FIG. 21

(1) Given a battery voltage $E = 1\cdot5$ V, find the shunt resistance of the meter so that the needle deflection is 100 divisions when the ohmmeter terminals are short-circuited.

(2) When the battery voltage falls ($E < 1\cdot5$ V), the ohmmeter zero can be set by adjusting the shunt, i.e. it can be arranged for the needle deflection to be 100 divisions when $r_x = 0$. Determine how far the battery voltage can fall.

(3) Find the magnitude of the resistance r_x corresponding to n scale divisions. Establish the connection between the scales of the ohmmeter and of the meter element.

(4) Find the error in determining a resistance if a reliable reading can only be made to half a scale division.

(5) In what way should the sizes of the resistances r_1 and r_2 be changed in order to widen the r_x measuring range 10 times, i.e. in order for the resistance as read on the ohmmeter scale to be 10 times less than the values of r_x?

118. What is the ratio of the arms l_1, l_2 of the bridge illustrated in Fig. 22 when it is balanced? The other two arms contain electric lamps as shown. In what conditions can this question be answered, when only the data marked on the lamp bases are available?

119. A voltage V is applied to a Wheatstone bridge. The galvanometer has a resistance R and indicates a current I, when resistances x, r_2, r_3, r_4 are connected in the arms of the bridge. Find the unknown resistance x.

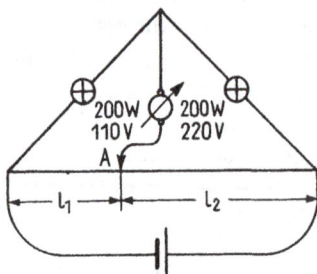

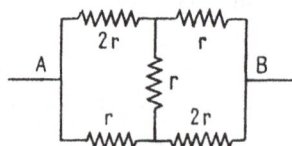

FIG. 22   FIG. 23

120. Find the resistance R between the points A and B for the circuit illustrated in Fig. 23. The resistances of the various branches are shown on the diagram.

121. Resistance measurements on a Wheatstone bridge have maximum accuracy when the resistances of adjacent arms are equal, i.e., when $R_1 = R_2$ (Fig. 24). Prove this for the case when the galvanometer resistance is very high, so that the current through the galvanometer is negligible.

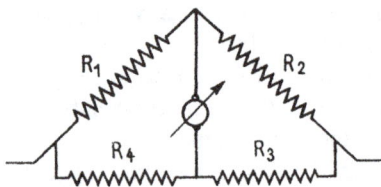

FIG. 24

Hint. Find the relationship between the relative variation in R_x and the voltage variation ΔV at the galvanometer.

122. Is a bridge balance destroyed if the current source and the galvanometer change places? Is the sensitivity affected?

123. In the Wheatstone bridge of Fig. 22, the scale position of the slider A on the slide wire enables the unknown resistance to be determined directly in ohms, if a constant 1 ohm resistance is connected in the right-hand arm. What are the corresponding resistances when the slider is located at $\frac{1}{3}$, $\frac{2}{3}$, $\frac{3}{4}$ the length of the slide wire from its left-hand end? Also, where is the slider located if the unknown resistance is equal to 1 ohm, 10 ohm? Draw the relevant graph. Find the absolute and relative error in the resistance determination, assuming that there is a constant error in determining the position of the slider A, amounting to 0·1 per cent of the length of the slide wire.

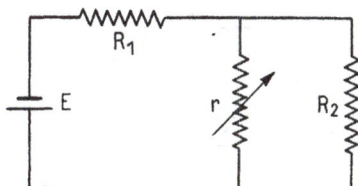

FIG. 25

124. Figure 25 illustrates a circuit in which r is a variable resistance. Draw a graph of the current through R_1 as a function of the resistance r. The quantities E, R_1 and R_2 are given.

125. If the scale of a pointer galvanometer, internal resistance 150 ohm, is divided into a hundred divisions, each worth 1 μamp, what shunt resistance R must be used in order for currents up to 1 mamp to be measured?

126. When a current of 0·1 mamp flows through a voltmeter with a 100 V scale, a reading of 1 V is obtained. If a 90,000 ohm resistance is added in series, what is the maximum potential difference V that the meter can read?

127. Two series-connected rheostats, each of resistance r = 5000 ohm, are connected across a battery of accumulators of e.m.f. $E = 6$ V. What will be the reading of a voltmeter connected to the terminals of one rheostat, if the voltmeter resistance is (1) $R = 100,000$ ohm; (2) $R = 10,000$ ohm (the internal resistance of the battery is small)?

128. A voltmeter connected between the terminals of a circuit connected to d.c. source indicates a potential difference of 50 V;

another voltmeter between the same terminals indicates 51 V, whilst an electrostatic voltmeter reads 52 V. The electrostatic voltmeter, connected on open circuit, reads 65 V. Find the resistance of the circuit, the internal resistance of the source and the resistance of the second voltmeter, if the first has a resistance of 6500 ohm.

129. By mistake, two galvanic cells with different e.m.f.'s $E_1 = 1\cdot9$ V, and $E_2 = 1\cdot1$ V, and with internal resistances $r_1 = 0\cdot1$ ohm and $r_2 = 0\cdot8$ ohm, were connected in parallel in a circuit. The cells were loaded by an external resistance of $R = 10$ ohm

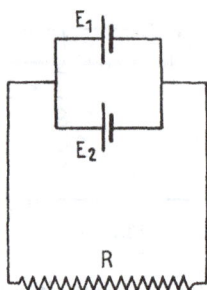

FIG. 26

(Fig. 26). What are the magnitudes and directions of the currents i_1, i_2 flowing through the cells, and what is the voltage V across the external resistance R?

130. A moving-iron instrument of internal resistance r_i in which each scale division is worth I_0 amp is employed as a voltmeter in conjunction with a series resistance R. What is each division worth in volts?

131. The scale division value of an instrument is 10 μamp. The scale has 100 divisions, the internal resistance is 100 ohm. How can the instrument be made into a voltmeter reading up to 100 V, or an ammeter reading current up to 1 amp?

132. A battery of e.m.f. E and internal resistance r is connected with two parallel resistances R_1 and R_2. Find (1) the current I through the battery; (2) the current I_1 through the resistance R_1; (3) the relative change in the current I_1 if the resistance R_2 is disconnected (consider the particular case when $r \ll R_1$)?

133. An instrument designed for 20 V operation has to be fed from 120 V d.c. mains, and it is required that, when the instrument resistance varies from 100 to 90 ohm, the potential difference across the instrument shall not vary by more than 1 per cent. Is it possible to do this by using a potentiometer?

134. Two identical galvanic cells of e.m.f. 1·5 V and internal resistance 2 ohm are connected as shown in Fig. 27. What is the

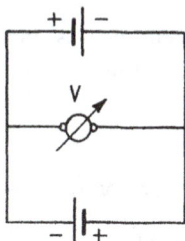

FIG. 27

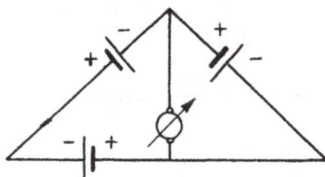

FIG. 28

current flowing through the cells? What is the reading of the voltmeter V? Neglect the resistance of the connecting wires.

135. What is the reading of the voltmeter in the previous problem if the internal resistance of one cell is 3 ohm, and of the other 1 ohm?

136. What is the reading of a voltmeter connected with three identical galvanic cells as shown in Fig. 28? As in the previous problems, neglect the resistance of the connecting wires.

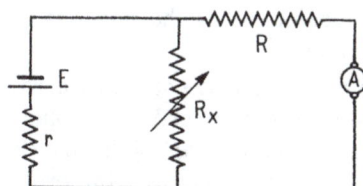

FIG. 29

137. Find the conditions under which the current supplied by two distinct series-connected galvanic cells, of e.m.f.'s E, E' and internal resistances ϱ and ϱ' respectively, will be less than the current supplied by the first, when they are connected to the same external resistance R.

138. What are the relative values of the resistances r, R_x and R in the circuit illustrated in Fig. 29 if the meter indicates a very small change in current for substantial variation of the resistance R_x? (Neglect the internal resistance of the source.)

139. In the circuit illustrated in Fig. 30, the batteries are connected in opposition, their e.m.f.'s are $E_1 = 1.5$ V, $E_2 = 1$ V, and the resistances are $R = 100$ ohm, $R_1 = 50$ ohm and $R_2 = 80$ ohm. Find the current through the resistance R.

140. What are the relationships between the resistances and e.m.f.'s in the circuit of Fig. 30 if no current flows through the second battery?

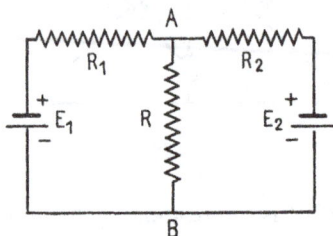

FIG. 30

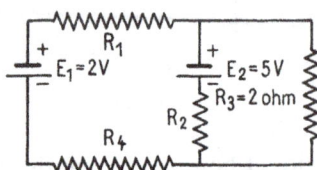

FIG. 31

141. The resistances are chosen for the circuit, the data of which are illustrated in Fig. 31, in such a way that no current flows through the battery with e.m.f. E_1. What is the voltage V_2 across the resistance R_2 and the current I_3 through the resistance R_3? The internal resistances of the batteries can be neglected.

142. The same conditions as the previous problem. Find the resistances R_2, R_1 and R_4.

143. A battery of e.m.f. E is connected across a slide wire of length L and resistance R, equipped with a slider. A voltmeter of resistance r is connected between the slider and one end of the slide wire. What is the relationship between the reading V of the voltmeter and the position of the slider?

144. Since identical galvanic cells were not available, two were joined in parallel with e.m.f.'s E_1, E_2 and internal resistances r_1, r_2. They supplied a current to an external circuit of resistance R. Find the e.m.f. E and internal resistance r of a cell which will supply the same current into the external circuit independently of the resistance R, and show that E is always less than the greater of the e.m.f.'s E_1, E_2.

145. In the circuit illustrated in Fig. 32, the resistances R_1, R_2, R_3 and the current I_3 through R_3 are known. Find the currents I_1, I_2 through the resistances R_1, R_2 and the e.m.f. E of the battery.

146. In the circuit illustrated in Fig. 33, all the resistances and the current I_4 through the resistance R_4 are known. Find the e.m.f. E of the battery. Neglect the internal resistance of the battery.

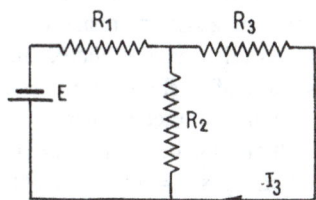

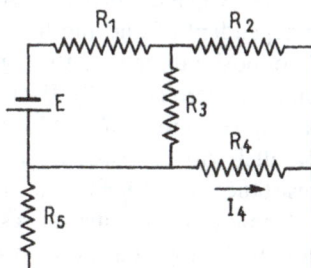

FIG. 32   FIG. 33

147. In the d.c. circuit of Fig. 34, $E = 10$ V, $R_1 = 5$ ohm, $R_2 = R_2' = 1$ ohm, $r = r' = 3$ ohm. The internal resistance of the battery can be neglected. Find the current in each branch.

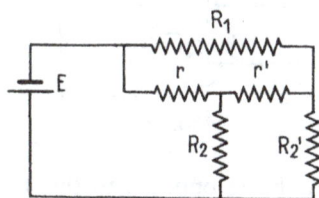

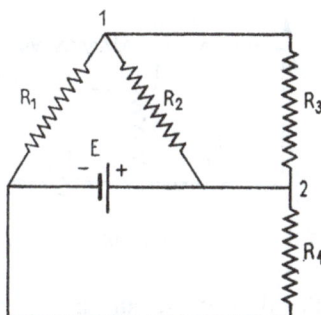

FIG. 34   FIG. 35

148. What is the e.m.f. E of the battery (in the circuit of Fig. 34, with the resistance values of the previous problem), if the current through the battery is known to be 3·24 amp?

149. In the circuit illustrated in Fig. 35, the resistances R_1, R_2 and R_3 are known, as also the battery current I and the potential difference $V_{2,1}$ between the points 2 and 1. Find the resistance R_4.

150. The circuit of Fig. 36 can be used for determining the internal resistance of a galvanic cell. The galvanometer G with known resistance R gives the same indications whether the moving contact is at B or C, the resistance AB being specially selected for this purpose. Let the resistance AB be known and equal to r. What is the internal resistance ϱ of the galvanic cell?

151. A galvanometer possesses two coils which are identical and independent of one another, so that, when the same current passes in opposite directions through the two coils, the galvanometer remains at zero (Fig. 37). Each coil, including its auxiliary resistance, has a resistance $R = 150,000$ ohm. The coil I is connected in parallel with a resistance r that forms part of a rheostat with a resistance $\varrho = 10,000$ ohm, the rheostat being connected across a galvanic cell, the internal resistance of which can be neglected. In conjunction with a rotary switch, the cell charges $n = 40$ times per second a condenser C, which in turn discharges via the switch at the same frequency through the coil II of the galvanometer, the

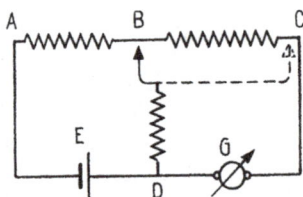

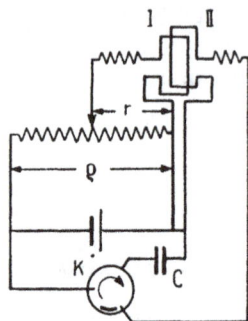

FIG. 36   FIG. 37

direction of the current through coil II being opposite to the direction through coil I. The resistance r is adjusted so that the galvanometer remains at zero, when $r = 3000$ ohm. What is the capacity of the condenser C?

152. A leakage to earth of known resistance r develops on a single-wire telegraph route (Fig. 38). Show that the current I at the receiving end of the line is a minimum when the fault is at the midpoint of the line. The resistance of the receiving equipment is small compared with the total line resistance.

153. A corridor is lit by a single bulb half way down it; how is the wiring arranged so that a person entering at either end can switch the light on or off, regardless of the switch position at the other end?

154. A device consists of a cylindrical pipe made of a material of poor conductivity. The pipe length is l, its inner and outer radii are R_1 and R_2, the specific resistance of the material is ϱ. Both cylindrical surfaces of the pipe are covered by layers of ideal conductor and a potential difference is produced between the layers, so that current flows through the pipe walls. Find the resistance r of the device.

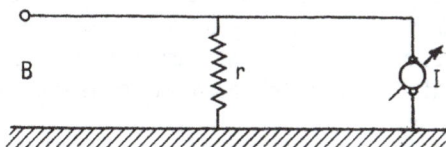

FIG. 38

155. A spherical shell, formed by concentric spheres of ideal conductor, is filled by a material of specific resistance ϱ. What is the resistance R of the spherical layer if its external and internal radii are r_1, r_2?

156. Show that the resistance of a uniform conducting medium filling the whole of the space between two ideally conducting envelopes of arbitrary shape is equal to $\varrho/4\pi C$, where ϱ is the specific resistance of the medium, and C is the capacity between the envelopes.

157. Two metal spheres of the same radius r are submerged in a homogeneous medium with specific resistance ϱ. What is the resistance R of the medium between the spheres? Assume that the distance between the spheres is very large compared with their radii.

158. Compare the voltages V_1 and V_2 at the terminals, and the powers W_1, W_2 delivered into an external circuit by the following two current generators: (1) a battery of $n = 50$ cells connected in series and each of e.m.f. $E = 2$ V, the load resistance being $R_1 = 200$ ohm, and the internal resistance per cell $r = 0 \cdot 2$ ohm; (2) an induction apparatus with multiple discs, producing a potential difference of 100,000 V on the spherical conductors and having an internal resistance of 10^8 ohm when connected to a load of resistance

$R_2 = 10^5$ ohm. How do the currents and powers in the loads change when the load resistances are doubled?

159. Compare the voltages and powers in the external load produced by: (1) a d.c. dynamo with very low internal resistance, supplying 5·5 amp into a load of 20 ohm resistance; (2) the battery of cells of the previous problem, connected to the same 20 ohm load. What change is there in the results of this comparison if the load resistance is halved?

160. A battery of e.m.f. $E = 40$ V and internal resistance $R = 5$ ohm is connected across an external resistance r that varies from zero to 35 ohm. Draw graphs on the same figure of the following functions of the external resistance: (a) the power supplied to the external resistance; (b) the power consumed in the source; (c) the total power.

161. An electric lamp is designed for a voltage V and consumes W watts. The filament of the lamp can be regarded as a cylinder of length l and radius r. What length and radius must be used for a filament of the same material in order for the lamp to dissipate W' watts at V' volts? Assume that the temperature of incandescence of the filament is the same in both cases and that the cooling of the filament is proportional to its surface area.

162. Due to vaporisation at the high temperature of incandescence a filament diameter diminishes in the course of time. If the diameter decreases by p per cent, how must the filament voltage be varied (increase or decrease?) in order for the filament temperature to remain as before? The cooling of the filament is proportional to its surface area.

163. Energy is to be sent along a mains of length 5 km from a 110 V supply of capacity 5 kW. What is the minimum diameter required for the copper wire if the energy loss in the mains is not to exceed 10 per cent of the power of the source? The specific resistance of copper is $0·017 \times 10^{-4}$ ohm cm.

164. Energy $N = 5000$ kW has to be sent a distance of 5 km from a source with a voltage $E = 100,000$ V.

The permissible voltage loss in the mains is $n = 1$ per cent. Find the minimum cross-section s of the copper wire of the mains. The specific resistance ϱ of copper is $0·017 \times 10^{-4}$ ohm cm. Compare with the results of the previous problem.

165. How many times must the source voltage be increased in order to obtain a 100 times reduction in the power loss in the line when sending the same power, given that the voltage drop in the line in the first case is $\Delta V = nV$, where V is the voltage at the load?

166. The Russian electrical engineer M. O. Dolivo-Dobrovol'skii proposed the three-wire d.c. system illustrated in Fig. 39 (a). The advantage of this system lies in reducing the amount of copper required for the line joining the source and load. To appreciate this advantage, we compare the two systems (a) and (b) of Fig. 39, transmitting the same power*.

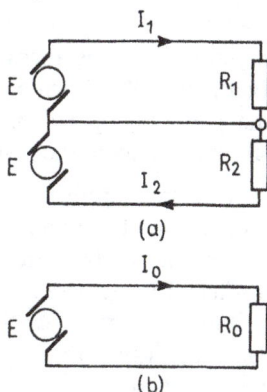

Fig. 39

(1) Find the relative reduction in the weight of the conductors in the Dolivo-Dobrovol'skii system under the following conditions: the loads in system (a) are symmetrical, i.e. $R_1 = R_2$; the transmitted powers and the power losses in the mains are the same for both systems; all the wires have the same cross-section in each system; the lengths and material of the wires are the same.

(2) Calculate the power loss ratio for the two systems when the load in system (a) is asymmetric, on the assumption that the resistance of the conductors is chosen by starting from the conditions stated in section (1), and the generator powers of the two systems are the same. Find the power loss ratio as a function of

$$\alpha = I_1/I_2.$$

* To give practical effect to the system, Dolivo-Dobrovol'skii specially built a d.c. machine with a voltage divider, so that one machine was employed instead of the two illustrated in Fig. 39.

167. We are given three electric lamps designed for 110 V, with powers of 50, 50 and 100 W. How can these lamps be arranged across a 220 V supply so that they all burn at full incandescence?

168. A voltage $V = 120$ V is supplied to the corridor of an apartment house. A 100 W lamp burns half way along the corridor and another 100 W lamp at the far end. The distance from the entrance to the second lamp at the far end is $L = 20$ m. What is the change in the power consumed by the lamps if an electric heater consuming a current $I = 5$ amp is installed half way between the lamps? The wire cross-section is $s = 2$ mm^2 (neglect the change in the lamp resistances).

169. In addition to certain other resistances, a circuit contains a resistance R_0 dissipating a power W. When an identical resistance is shunted across R_0 the power dissipated in the two is still W. Draw the simplest circuit and calculate the resistances.

170. Find the law of the temperature rise of a manganin wire carrying d.c. Use Newton's law of cooling, i.e. assume that the amount of heat given off by unit surface area of the wire in unit time is $Q = k(T - T_0)$, where T is the wire temperature and T_0 the temperature of the surrounding medium. At the initial instant the wire temperature is equal to T_0. The wire resistance is R, its length l, its radius of cross-section r, its density d, its specific heat c. The current through the conductor is constant and equal to I. The resistance of manganin is independent of the temperature.

171. A potential difference V, maintained constant, is applied to the electrodes of an electrolytic bath. The electrolyte resistance varies with temperature in accordance with the law

$$R_T = R_0/(1 + \alpha T).$$

Assuming that the cooling of the electrolyte is subject to Newton's law (see the previous problem), find the stationary temperature of the electrolyte. The surface area of the electrolyte is S and the temperature of the surrounding medium T_0. The mass of the electrolyte and its specific heat are assumed constant.

172. What is the dependence on time of the power W supplied by the current in a graphite rod with a constant voltage V across it, if the temperature dependence of the resistance R of graphite is

$$R = R_0/(1 + \alpha T)$$

and if the rod cools in accordance with Newton's law (see Problem 170)? The mass of the graphite is m, its specific heat is c, its surface area S, its initial temperature and the temperature of the surrounding medium T_0.

§ 3. PERMANENT MAGNETS

173. Three identical magnetic needles are arranged at the vertices of an equilateral triangle. The needles can rotate about axes perpendicular to the plane of the triangle. All other effects and the Earth's magnetic field can be neglected. The needle length is much less than the side of the triangle. What is the equilibrium position of the needles?

174. A magnetic needle has a magnetic moment M (the direction of the magnetic moment coincides with the direction of the needle axis from the south to the north pole).

Find the potential V and the magnetic field-strength at a point A, located at a distance d from the mid-point of the needle in a direction φ relative to the needle axis. What is the angle θ between the direction of the field at the point A and the radius vector d? The magnetic permeability of the medium is μ. The distance d is much greater than the length l of the needle.

FIG. 40

175. A magnetic needle with a moment M is located in a uniform magnetic field of field-strength H, and forms an angle θ with the direction of the field. In this case, what is the potential energy E_{pot} of the needle in the field?

176. Two identical thin magnets are separated by a distance which is n times the length of each of them. What is the force F of mutual attraction if each has magnetic moment M and length l, and they are mounted with opposite poles facing along a straight line? The magnetic permeability of the medium is 1 and $n \gg 1$.

177. Find the period of vibration T of the magnets of the previous problem if they are brought close together so that the distance between them is $n = 20$ times less than the length of each and they are each made to deviate towards the same direction by a small angle φ, as shown in Fig. 40, then are let free. The magnets are mounted on their axes without friction and the moment of inertia of each about its axis is I.

178. Does the period of vibration increase or decrease if the magnets (see the previous problem) are deflected in different directions through the same small angle at the initial instant, as indicated in Fig. 41, before being set free?

179. A thin magnetised rod is suspended from one end in a uniform vertical magnetic field. The magnetic moment of the rod is $M = 49$ e.m.u., its mass is $m = 6$ g, its length $l = 100$ mm. Find the magnitude and direction of the field H, if the period of vibration T of the magnet is twice its period of vibration in the absence of the magnetic field.

180. The magnetic moment of a compass needle is M, its weight P, its length l. The horizontal component of the earth's field is H. Regard the needle as a thin rod and find its period of vibration T in the earth's field.

181. A magnet of magnetic moment M in the shape of a rod of weight p and radius R is suspended from its mid-point by a thread

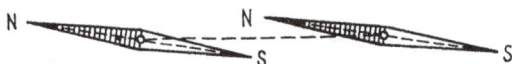

FIG. 41

as follows. A very small hole, in which the thread is clamped, is drilled through the mid-point of the rod perpendicular to its axis. What position does the magnet take up in the earth's magnetic field if the horizontal and vertical components of the latter are H, H_V respectively?

182. The field-strength in the narrow gap of a magnet (Fig. 42) is $H = 400$ oersted. What is the field-strength H_0 in the material of the magnet close to the gap, if the permeability of the material is $\mu = 500$?

183. The magnetisation vector I in a rectangular bar is the same at all points of the bar and is directed along its axis (Fig. 43). Find the surface density σ of the magnetic charge at the ends of the bar and the ratio B/H inside the bar.

184. A magnetic needle consists of a thin straight steel spoke of length $l = 6$ cm and mass $m = 1$ g. The needle can rotate freely about a vertical axis through its centre of gravity. After being taken from its position of equilibrium it performs vibrations in the earth's magnetic field. Show that these vibrations are harmonic (for small angles of deviation). Find the magnetic moment M of the needle, given that the period of vibration is $T = 5$ sec and the horizontal component of the earth's field is $H = 0.2$ oersted.

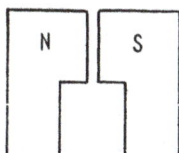

Fig. 42

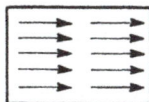

Fig. 43

185. A horseshoe permanent magnet whose circular section has diameter $D = 2$ cm can support an anchorage and load that together weigh $P = 10$ kg. Find the field-strength H close to the poles and the magnetic charge density at the poles.

186. A number of magnetic needles are mounted at equidistant points along a straight line. What are the possible positions of equilibrium and which of them are stable?

187. The horizontal component H of the earth's field can be determined as follows. Mount a short, powerful, rectangular bar magnet at its centre on a needle and find the period T of its small vibrations about the equilibrium position. Then arrange it perpendicularly to the earth's field in a horizontal plane and locate a short magnetic needle on the continuation of the axis of the bar at a distance d which is much greater than the length of the bar, and find the angle α between the needle and the bar axis. Knowing T, d and α, how is H calculated? Assume that the moment of inertia of the bar relative to a vertical axis through its centre is equal to I.

188. How can the magnetic moment M of the bar be found from the data of the previous problem?

§ 4. The Magnetic Field of a Current

189. A circular loop of radius R is made from a piece of insulated wire and connected to a current source of constant e.m.f. What is the change in the magnetic field-strength at the centre of the circle if the same piece of wire is used to make two adjacent loops each of radius $\frac{1}{2}R$?

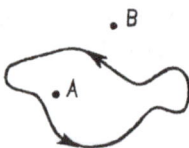

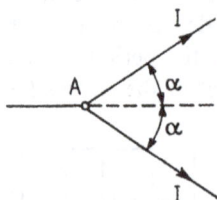

FIG. 44   FIG. 45

190. Current flows along a plane closed circuit of arbitrary shape (Fig. 44). Find the directions of the magnetic field at the point A inside the circuit and the point B outside the circuit.

191. A direct current I flows through the wall of a cylindrical pipe. What is the magnetic field-strength H inside and outside the pipe?

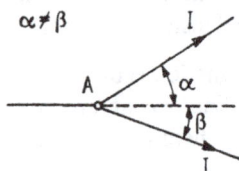

FIG. 46

192. A current I flows along a uniform right cylindrical conductor of radius R. Find the magnetic field-strength H inside and outside the conductor at a distance r from its axis.

193. Figure 45 illustrates a symmetrical current branching circuit. All the conductors are straight, infinite and coplanar. Find the magnetic field-strength on the line perpendicular to the plane of the currents through the point A when the current in each branch is equal to I.

194. Solve Problem 193 with the modification that can be seen in Fig. 46.

195. Find the magnetic field-strength in the plane of symmetry of a wire bent at a right angle (Fig. 47), on the line OAO' lying in the plane of the currents, and on the line perpendicular to this plane through the point A. Draw a rough sketch of the lines of force in the plane of symmetry.

196. A source of e.m.f. is joined to two opposite corners of a square-shaped plane conducting circuit. What is the magnetic field-strength H at the centre of the square produced by current flowing along its sides? (Neglect the field of the leads to the source.)

197. Find the magnetic field-strength H at the centre when a current I flows through a plane rectangular circuit of sides a, b.

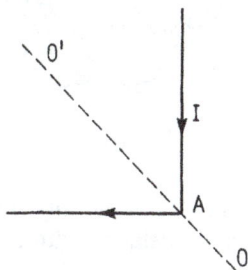

FIG. 47

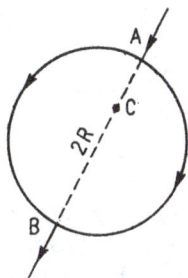

FIG. 48

198. Find the magnetic field-strength H at the centre of an equilateral triangle of side a through which a current I flows.

199. What is the magnetic field-strength H at the centre of an equilateral triangle of uniform wire when a source of e.m.f. is joined to two vertices of the triangle? (Neglect the field of the leads to the source.)

200. A source of e.m.f. is joined to opposite ends of a diameter AB of a circular conducting loop of radius R (Fig. 48). What is the magnetic field-strength H at an arbitrary point C of the diameter? (Neglect the field of the leads to the source.)

201. Fine wire is wound round a wooden sphere of radius R so that the turns lie on great circles that intersect at the ends of the same diameter AB (Fig. 49). There are six turns and the planes of two neighbouring turns form an angle of 30°. A current I flows through the turns. Find the magnitude and direction of the field-strength H at the centre of the sphere.

202. Four turns of wire are wound across a cylindrical wooden drum at an angle of 45° to one another; each turn forms a rectangle of side h (the length of the drum) and side $D = AB$ (the base diameter). The turns start and finish at the centre C of one of the bases

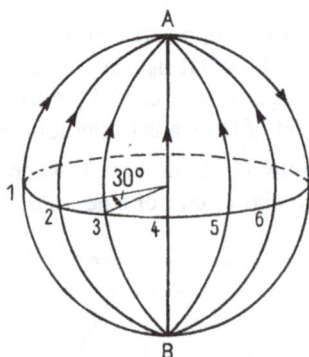

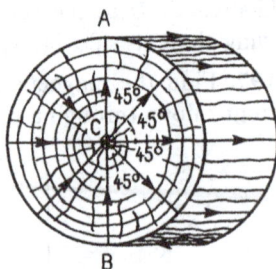

FIG. 49   FIG. 50

of the drum (Fig. 50). A current I flows through the wire. Find the magnitude and direction of the magnetic field-strength H at the midpoint of the cylinder axis.

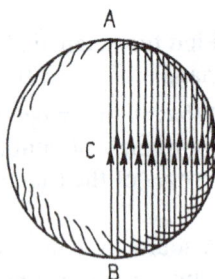

FIG. 51   FIG. 52

203. A conductor passes along the diameter of a great circle from the point A to the point B (Fig. 51) inside a uniform conducting sphere. A current I flows from B to A, then via the sphere back to the point B. Find the magnetic field-strength inside and outside the sphere produced by the current flowing through the conductor and sphere.

204. Fine wire is wound on a wooden sphere of radius R so that all the turns are parallel to one another. The turns are wound close together and form a layer covering half the sphere (Fig. 52). A current I flows through the wire. Find the magnetic field-strength H at the centre C of the sphere. The total number of turns is N. The turns can be regarded as rings equally spaced along the arc of the great circle whose plane is perpendicular to the plane of the rings.

205. Identical pieces of wire are soldered together to form a cube (Fig. 53). An e.m.f. is applied to opposite ends A and B of a diagonal. What is the magnetic field-strength H at the centre of the cube? (Neglect the field of the leads to the source.)

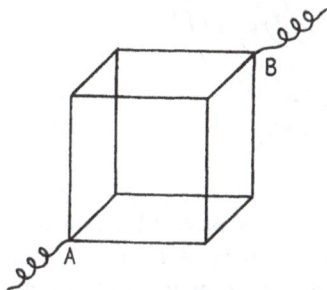

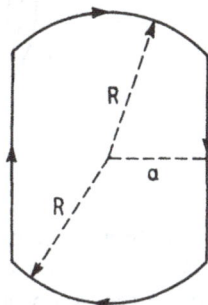

Fig. 53   Fig. 54

206. Find the magnetic field-strength H at the centre of the plane closed circuit illustrated in Fig. 54, through which a current I flows. The circuit is composed of two arcs of radius R and two straight pieces a distance $2a$ apart.

207. Find the magnetic field-strength H at the centre of a plane spiral through which a current I flows. The inner and outer radii of the spiral are r and R (Fig. 55). The total number of turns in the spiral is N. Neglect the field of the leads to the source.

208. Find the magnetic field-strength H on the axis of a solenoid at the point A at which the diameters of the ends subtend angles 2α and 2β (Fig. 56). The solenoid has N turns uniformly spaced along its length l and carries a current I.

209. For the previous problem, draw the graph of the magnetic field-strength H on the solenoid axis as a function of the distance x of the point A from the mid-point of the solenoid; use the following numerical data: $I = 1$ amp; $D = 2$ cm; $l = 1$ m; $N = 1000$; $x = 0; 25; 40; 45; 50; 60$ cm.

210. Two circular current loops of the same radius are separated at a distance equal to their diameter. The currents are equal and in the same direction. Draw the graph of the field-strength H along the line through their centres (Fig. 57).

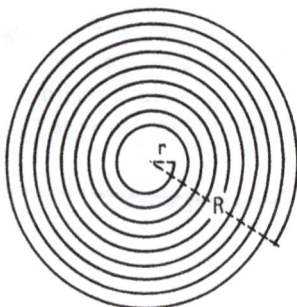

FIG. 55

211. A thin diamagnetic rod of mass $m = 0 \cdot 1$ g and suscepti-bility $k' = -14 \cdot 5 \times 10^{-6}$ is freely suspended from its centre of gravity on the axis of a circular current loop at a distance d (sub-stantially greater than the length of the rod) from the plane of the

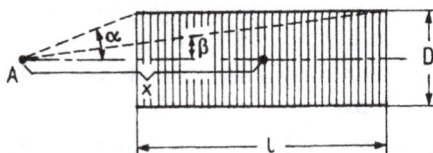

FIG. 56

loop (Fig. 58). The loop radius is $R = d = 10$ cm; the current $J = 100$ amp. What is the orientation of the rod and the resultant force F acting on it? The density of the rod material is $D = 9 \cdot 8$ gcm^{-3}.

212. A condenser of capacity $C = 1$ μF is switched mechanically at a rate of $N = 100$ times per second to the poles of a dynamo giving a voltage $V = 120$ V, and is discharged the same number of times per second through a tangent compass, consisting of $n = 100$ turns of radius $a = 15 \cdot 7$ cm. The horizontal component of the earth's field is $H = 0.2$ oersted. Find the angle of deviation of the magnetic needle.

213. What is the effect on the deviation of the needle of the tangent compass of the previous problem if resistance is present in the condenser–compass circuit?

214. Current from a battery of accumulators of negligible internal resistance flows through a rheostat of resistance $R = 10$ ohm in series with a tangent compass. A needle deviation $\alpha_1 = 60°$ is observed. An auxiliary resistance $r = 10$ ohm is introduced into the circuit, and the needle deviation falls to $\alpha_2 = 45°$. Find the resistance ϱ of the compass.

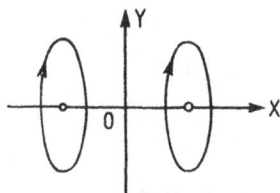
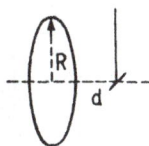

FIG. 57   FIG. 58

215. A tangent compass was not initially accurately set up in the plane of the magnetic meridian, so that, when current passed in one direction the needle deviated through an angle θ, and when current passed in the opposite direction the needle deviated in the opposite direction through an angle $\theta' \neq \theta$. Find the current I if the compass constant is k (the constant k is equal to the current at which the needle deviates 45°).

216. A plane rectangular wire frame can rotate about a vertical axis through the frame centre. The angle of rotation is shown on a dial by means of a pointer rigidly connected to the frame (Fig. 59). A magnetic needle is mounted on a vertical axis at the centre of the frame; initially the needle and frame are in the same plane. When a current of 1 amp passes the needle deviates, and the frame has to be turned through an angle $\theta = 30°$ in order for the needle to lie again in its plane. What currents can be measured by using this device?

217. Two mutually perpendicular circular loops, radii R, R' respectively have a common centre and are mounted in vertical planes; the plane of the first loop coincides with the plane of the

magnetic meridian. A short magnetic needle that can rotate freely
in a horizontal plane is mounted at the common centre of the
loops. The current in the loop in the plane of the magnetic meridian is I, and in the other loop I'. The magnetic needle is observed
to deviate through an angle θ. If the flow of the current I' is rever-
sed, the needle deviation is θ'. (1) What is the current I'? (2) What
is the horizontal component H of the earth's magnetic field?

218. Two mutually perpendicular circular loops and a magnetic
needle are arranged as in the previous problem. The currents are
equal. The observed needle deviation is θ. Find the current I, given
the horizontal component H of the earth's magnetic field.

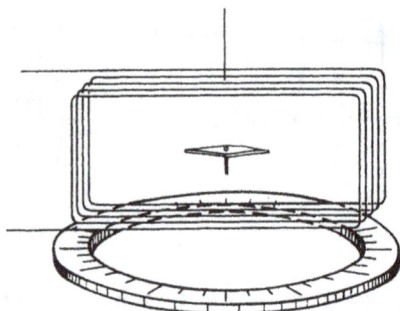

Fig. 59

219. A rectangular frame (rectangle area S) with n turns has a
bifilar suspension and is orientated in the plane of the magnetic
meridian. When d.c. is passed through the frame it rotates through
an angle θ. Find the current if the moment of the force that twists
the suspension through 1 radian is D.

220. The resistance of bismuth varies under the action of a magnetic field in accordance with Goldhammer's law

$$\Delta\varrho/\varrho = 3 \times 10^{-9}H^2,$$

where H is the field-strength in oersted. This property of bismuth
may be used for measuring magnetic fields. Find the accuracy with
which a field-strength of 4000 oersted can be measured, if the resistance of the bismuth spiral is of the order of 10 ohm and is
measured on an equal-arm bridge; an e.m.f. of 1 V is applied to one
diagonal of the bridge whilst a galvanometer with a sensitivity of

1×10^{-6} amp per division and a resistance of 200 ohm is connected across the other diagonal (assume that the bridge balance can be established to an accuracy of 1 galvanometer division).

221. A square conducting loop $ABCD$ (Fig. 60) is placed in the magnetic field of a long thin rod with a magnetic moment I_0 per unit volume and cross-section S, the north pole N of the magnet being at the centre of the square, whilst the magnet itself is perpendicular to the plane of the loop. A voltage source is connected to the

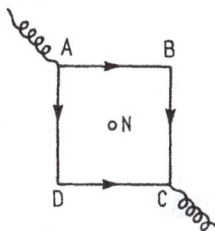

FIG. 60

ends A, C of a diagonal of the loop, with the result that a current I flows through the sides. Find the couple M rotating the loop, and its direction.

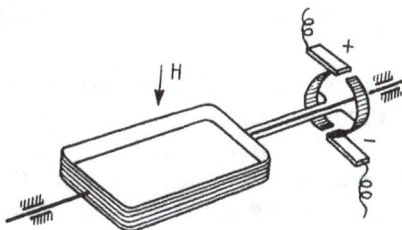

FIG. 61

222. A circular loop of radius R with a current I flowing clockwise through it (viewing from the north pole of the magnet) is located in the field of the magnet of the previous problem. The magnet lies along the axis of the loop, and its north pole is at a distance d from the loop centre. Find the forces acting on the loop from the magnet.

223. A frame of area S cm^2 that can rotate about its axis is located in a constant uniform field of strength H oersted. The frame axis is perpendicular to the direction of the field (Fig. 61). The frame carries n turns of wire, through which a current I amp flows via a collector. The collector switches the direction of the current at the instant when the plane of the frame is perpendicular to the direction of the magnetic field. Find the maximum work W that can be done by the frame when it turns through one revolution, given that the current I between switchings can be regarded as constant.

224. A magnet in the form of a long steel circular cylinder is mounted vertically. We assume for the purposes of calculation that

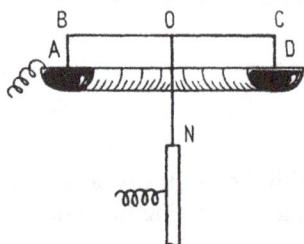

FIG. 62

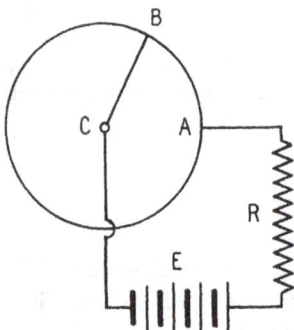

FIG. 63

a magnetic mass m is concentrated at its north pole N. A T-shaped wire frame $ABOCD$ is supported via the rod ON (Fig. 62) at the pole; the ends A, D of the frame are submerged in mercury, contained in a horizontal annular trough. The point O is at the centre of $BC = 2l$. The sections $AB = CD$ are small compared with l. A constant voltage is applied to the magnet and to the mercury in the trough, as a result of which a current $2I$ flows through the rod ON and the wire frame revolves about ON. The distance ON of BC from the pole N is equal to l. Find: (1) the moment of the couple turning the frame; (2) the point of application of the force acting on the arm OC.

225. The principle of operation of an electric motor can be understood by considering the model illustrated in Fig. 63. A fixed circular conducting loop is mounted horizontally in a vertical uniform magnetic field of H oersted. A metal rod CB of mass m and length l is supported on a vertical axis through the centre C of the circle and its other end touches the loop. A current is fed from a battery of e.m.f. E volt via a resistance R ohm to the rod at the point C and to the point A of the loop. Find the law governing the rise in the angular velocity ω of rotation of the rod after switching the current on if the moment of the friction forces opposing rotation of the rod is equal to $\alpha l^2 \omega$, where α is a constant coefficient of proportionality. The electrical resistances of the rod, the loop, the contacts and also the internal resistance of the battery can be neglected in comparison with the resistance R.

226. A mirror galvanometer has a rectangular wire coil (40 × 30 mm) containing 100 turns of fine wire, suspended by a thread, the coefficient of torsion of which is $0.001 \text{ gcm deg}^{-1}$. The coil is situated in the gap between the poles of a magnet producing a field $H = 1000$ oersted, which can be regarded as directed radially to the axis of rotation for all positions of the coil. (1) What is the angle α of deflection of the coil when a current of 0.1 m amp passes through it? (2) If a millimetre scale is mounted at a distance of 1 m from the mirror galvanometer, what current I corresponds to a spot deflection of 1 mm?

227. A rectangular frame can rotate about a vertical axis passing through the mid-points of opposite sides of the frame. The frame is located in a uniform horizontal magnetic field H and current passes through it. Find the equilibrium position of the frame and consider its stability.

228. A frame carrying n turns of fine wire is in the form of a square of side a. It can rotate about a vertical axis through the mid-points of opposite sides of the frame. A constant current i flows through the frame, which is situated in a uniform horizontal magnetic field H. (1) Find the direction of the current in the frame for stable equilibrium. (2) Find the period T of small vibration of the frame about this position, if the moment of inertia of the frame is I_0.

229. A single-layer coil is wound uniformly on an iron core of square section (side $a = 4$ cm) toroidal shape (the diameter $D = 40$ cm). The number of turns is $N = 500$. A current $I = 1$ amp flows through the coil. The permeability of iron is $\mu = 400$. Find the flux of induction through the core cross-section.

230. The toroidal core of the previous problem is split so as to contain an air gap of thickness $d = 1$ mm. Find the flux of induction Φ, neglecting the scattering of the lines of force.

231. An iron core has the same dimensions as in the previous two problems. If it has an air gap $d_1 = 1$ mm, at a certain current the flux of induction is $\Phi_1 = 3000$ Mx. When the air gap is increased to $d_2 = 2$ mm, the flux of induction is $\Phi_2 = 2500$ Mx for the same current. Assuming that scattering of the lines of force can be neglected in both cases, find the permeability μ of the iron.

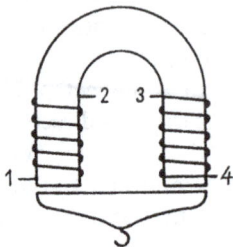

FIG. 64

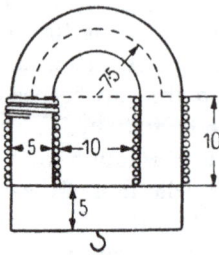

FIG. 65

232. An accumulator feeds the coils of the electromagnet illustrated in Fig. 64. With what connection of the coils (series or parallel) will the lifting force of the electromagnet be the greater, and by how many times? Mention which ends have to be joined in the different types of connection. The two coils are identical in all respects.

233. A horseshoe electromagnet of square-section iron has the dimension indicated in Fig. 65 in centimetres. The number of turns on the coil is $N = 200$. The current is $I = 2$ amp. What is the lifting force F if $\mu = 200$?

234. The armature of the electromagnet of the previous problem carries a load of 20 kg and is separated from the core by a distance of 1 mm. What current I must pass through the coil in order for the electromagnet to attract the armature?

235. A short coil of cross-section S, carrying N turns, is mounted inside a long coil (Fig. 66) carrying n turns per centimetre length; the axis of the short coil is perpendicular to the axis of the long coil and is arranged vertically. The inner coil is clamped to the arm of a balance which is in equilibrium in the absence of current. When the same current I flows through both coils, a load P has to be placed on the longer arm of the balance to restore equilibrium. The length of the arm carrying the load is L. Find the current I.

236. Regarding the device of the previous problem, what effect does a substantial reduction in the length of the long coil have on the readings of the device if the number n remains constant?

FIG. 66

237. In what circumstances is it possible to measure alternating current with the aid of the device described in Problem 235? What sort of currents will the device indicate?

238. Can the device described in Problem 235 be used as a watt-meter?

239. A current I flows in a long coil carrying n turns per cm. Find the pressure p acting on the lateral surface of the solenoid.

240. Why do two parallel wires carrying current in the same direction attract one another, whilst two parallel cathode beams repel one another?

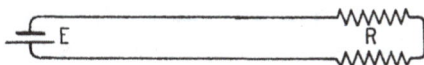

FIG. 67

241. Current flows from a voltage source E along two long parallel wires, connected to a load R (Fig. 67). Draw a sketch of the electric and magnetic fields in the plane perpendicular to the plane of the wires.

242. One side of a voltage source E is connected to two straight parallel wires, which are in turn connected via a resistance R and a return lead remote from the two parallel wires to the other side of the source (Fig. 68). What are the electric and magnetic fields in the plane perpendicular to the plane of the two parallel wires?

243. A current of 1 amp flows along a long pin clamped horizontally. What must be the spacing d between the pin and a long bare copper wire parallel to it in the same vertical plane in order for the magnetic interaction to balance the weight of the wire, if a current of i amps flows along the latter in the same direction? The weight of the wire is P, its length l.

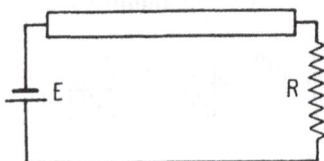

FIG. 68

244. A straight wire of length l cm is suspended below a long horizontal pin by means of two identical springs (the coefficient of stiffness of each spring is k dyn cm^{-1}) (Fig. 69). The distance between the pin and wire is h cm when no current is flowing. Find the distance x between them when a current of I amps flows through the pin, and i amps through the wire. Consider the two cases: (1) the currents are in the same direction, (2) the currents flow in opposite directions. The wire can only move in a vertical plane.

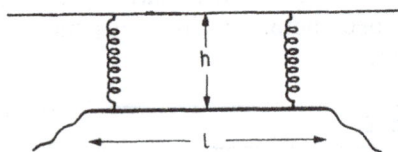

FIG. 69

245. A flat trough is mounted between the poles of a powerful magnet. Two parallel vertical tubes leave the narrow walls of the trough. Platinum electrodes A (+) and K (−) issue from the top and bottom of the trough and are connected via a switch R to a source of e.m.f. E. The trough and the tubes are filled with a conducting liquid, and the liquid level is at the same height in both tubes (Fig. 70). What happens when the switch is closed?

246. The device described in the previous problem can be employed for measuring currents. Find the current i flowing through the liquid in the trough if the magnetic induction of the field is B, the width of the trough is d, the stationary-state difference in the levels is h, the density of the liquid is ϱ. What is the sensitivity of the device dependent on?

247. A U-tube is mounted between the poles of a powerful electromagnet, in such a way that one limb (capillary) is in the field, and the other (wide) limb is outside the field. Liquid of permeability $\varkappa$ and density d is poured into the tube. What change occurs in the

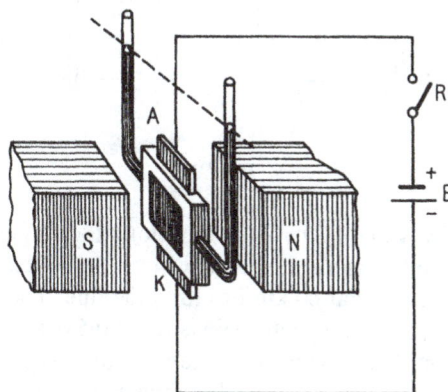

Fig. 70

level in the capillary when a field of intensity H is switched on? The susceptibility of the vapour and air above the liquid can be regarded as 1.

§ 5. ELECTROMAGNETIC INDUCTION

248. Two parallel wires joined at one end are mounted in a uniform magnetic field with induction B so that the plane of the wires is perpendicular to the field (Fig. 71(a)). A metal bridge is arranged to slide (without friction) along the wires. If the bridge is set in motion with constant velocity v, an induced e.m.f. E_i and an electric current I_i are produced in the circuit formed by the wires and bridge. A force F has to be applied to the bridge in order to maintain its velocity v. Deduce the law of induction by starting from Lenz's law and using the law of interaction between currents and a magnetic field.

Hint. The law established by the St. Petersburg Academician Lenz enables the following assertion to be made. If we clamp the bridge and include a battery in the circuit (Fig. 71(b)) which produces a current I equal to the current I_t obtained when the bridge moves, the force F_1 acting on the bridge will be equal in magnitude and opposite in direction to the force which has to be applied in the first case, in order to maintain the motion of the bridge.

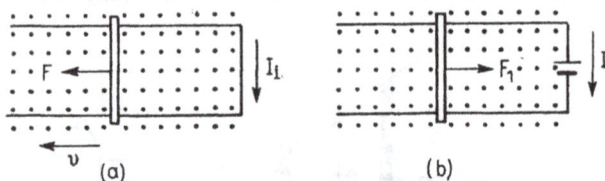

FIG. 71

249. A railway line 1·2 m wide runs along the magnetic meridian, and its rails can be assumed insulated from each other and from the earth. A train travels at 60 km/hr along the line. The vertical component of the earth's magnetic field is $H_v = 0·5$ oersted. What is the reading of a millivoltmeter connected at some point between the rails (1) when the train is approaching the meter, (2) when it is passing over the meter, (3) when it is travelling away from the meter?

250. Given the conditions of the previous problem, will the millivoltmeter reading be affected by the horizontal component of the earth's field if the line is curved?

251. A rectangular frame of sides a, b moves uniformly with velocity v in a direction perpendicular to an infinitely long straight wire, lying in the plane of the frame parallel to the side b. A current I flows in the wire. Find the e.m.f. E induced in the frame, and the direction of the induced current.

252. The rectangular frame of the previous problem rotates with constant angular velocity about its side b, which is at a distance $c > a$ from the wire carrying the current. Will the e.m.f. induced in the frame be sinusoidal?

253. A rectangular frame ($a \times b$) rotates uniformly with angular velocity ω about the side a in a uniform alternating magnetic field which varies sinusoidally with angular frequency ω' and is perpen-

dicular to the axis of rotation of the frame. Find the magnitude of
the induced e.m.f. E. Consider the particular cases when $\omega = \omega'$
and (1) at the initial instant $H = H_0$, whilst the plane of the frame
is perpendicular to H; (2) at the initial instant $H = H_0$, and the
frame is parallel to H.

254. A rectangular frame ($a \times b$) rotates about one of its sides
in a uniform magnetic field of intensity H, perpendicular to the
axis of rotation. with variable angular velocity $\omega = \omega_0(1 - e^{-kt})$.
Find the magnitude of the induced e.m.f. E, if the frame is perpendicular to the field at the initial instant.

255. The St. Petersburg professor of physics I. I. Borgman determined the susceptibility of a weakly magnetic liquid by submerging
two coils, rigidly coupled together, in the liquid. By comparing the

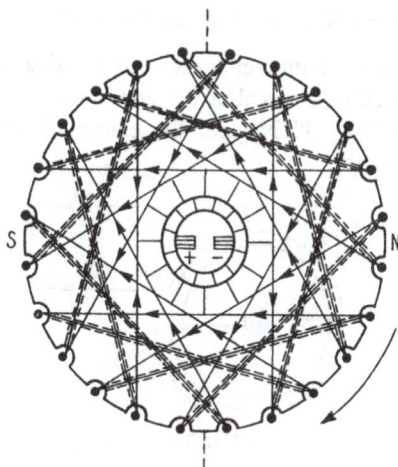

Fig. 72

e.m.f. induced in one of the coils by the current varying in the other,
firstly when surrounded by liquid, then secondly when surrounded
by air, the susceptibility of the liquid could be found. It was found
in one experiment that the induced e.m.f. was $E_1 = 24{\cdot}04$ V for
the coils submerged in a solution of ferric chloride, the corresponding e.m.f. for the coils in air being $E_2 = 24{\cdot}00$ V. Find the susceptibility of the solution.

256. A motor armature has a drum winding consisting of 20 series connected sections, each of which consists of 30 turns of rectangular shape (25 × 20 cm) of thin wire. (The arrangement of the winding is illustrated for 12 sections in Fig. 72.) The armature is situated in a uniform magnetic field with induction 3980 oersted. The armature is connected to 120 V d.c. mains via a commutator, and the motor turns at 600 r.p.m. (1) What is the current in the armature (the armature resistance is 0·5 ohm)? (2) What would happen if the armature were suddenly stopped?

257. A copper disc of radius $a = 10$ cm rotates at $N = 100$ rev/sec in a uniform magnetic field. The direction of the field is perpendicular to the plane of the disc and the field-strength is $H = 10^4$ oersted. The disc is connected via two brushes, one on the axis and one on the circumference, to an external circuit consisting of a rheostat of resistance $R = 10$ ohm and an ammeter of negligible internal resistance. What is the reading of the ammeter?

258. What will the ammeter indicate if the disc in the previous problem is replaced by a wheel of the same radius with two spokes, as illustrated in Fig. 73? Neglect the electrical resistance of the material of the wheel.

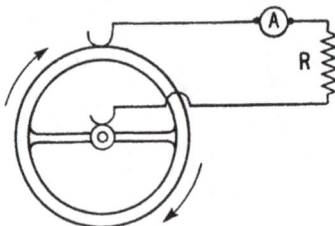

FIG. 73

259. The following method has been proposed for measuring resistance in absolute units. A long coil (n turns per unit length) is connected in circuit with an e.m.f. E and a resistance R (Fig. 74). A small coil with N turns and cross-section S rotates with constant angular velocity ω inside the long coil about an axis perpendicular to the axis of the long coil. At the instants when the e.m.f. induced in the small coil is a maximum its ends are connected via a galvanometer G across the resistance R. The latter is chosen in such a way that there is no current through the galvanometer. Find R.

260. A square frame of side $a = 5$ cm, carrying a few turns of copper wire of cross-section $S = 0.5$ mm^2, rotates slowly in a uniform magnetic field of induction $B = 8400$ oersted. The ends of the frame are short-circuited. The maximum of the current induced in the frame when it rotates is $I = 1.9$ amp. (1) Find the number of revolutions of the frame per second. (2) What change must be made in the speed of rotation of the frame in order for the current in the circuit to remain unchanged when the copper wire is replaced by iron wire?

261. The magnetic flux increases uniformly with time inside a long circular iron rod. There is no magnetic field outside the rod. Find the electric field outside the rod.

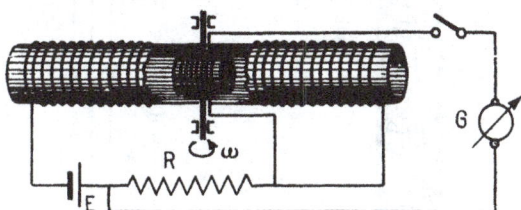

FIG. 74

262. The rod of the previous problem is encircled by a coil of wire connected across an ammeter. The resistance of the coil plus ammeter is R. (1) What does the ammeter indicate? (2) What is the direction of the current in the coil?

263. An electron is located at a distance from the iron rod (Problem 261). Its initial velocity is zero. Determine its motion.

264. A long single-layer coil with iron core is split into two sections (Fig. 75). Measurements of the inductances of the sections gave the following results: for the first section $L_1 = 0.04$ H, for the second section $L_2 = 0.09$ H. (1) What is the inductance L of the entire coil? (2) How many turns are there on the coil if the first section has 100 turns?

265. How can the inductance of a long coil be determined by passing d.c. through it?

266. Find the inductance of the conductor illustrated in Fig. 76. The current flows along a wire of 1 mm diameter mounted on the axis of the thin metal tube and soldered to the centre of the tube bottom, then returns via the tube surface. The dimensions of the tube are shown in the sketch.

267. The same current flows in opposite directions along two long parallel wires. Both wires have the same circular section of radius $r = 2$ mm and are spaced $d = 2$ cm apart. Find the inductance L per unit length of this two-wire system, assuming the magnetic field only exists outside the wires.

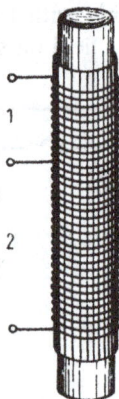

FIG. 75

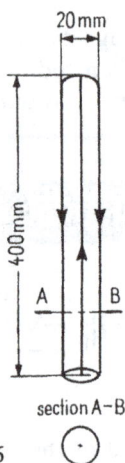

FIG. 76

268. Two coils are wound on the same core. The inductances of the individual coils are $L_1 = 0·5$ H and $L_2 = 0·7$ H. What is their mutual inductance M? Neglect leakage of the magnetic field.

269. Two windings (1, 1') and (2, 2') are close wound on a long cylinder as illustrated in Fig. 77. The inductance of each winding is 0·05 H. What is the inductance of the entire circuit if (1) the ends 1' and 2' are joined and the measurement is across the ends 1 and 2? (2) the ends 1 and 2' are joined, and the measurement is across the ends 1' and 2? (3) the ends 1', 2' and 1, 2 respectively are joined, and the measurement is across these two pairs of joined ends?

270. What is the energy W of the magnetic field of a solenoid of N turns, single-layer wound, carrying a current I? The length of the solenoid is l, its cross-section is S (the diameter of the cross-section is small compared to l).

271. Two long parallel conductors are spaced 20 cm apart. A current of 20 amp is maintained through one conductor, and an equal current is maintained in the opposite direction through the other. (1) If the conductors are moved apart to a distance of 40 cm, what is the work done by the magnetic field per unit length of the conductors? (2) What change occurs in the magnetic energy per unit length of the system?

272. In the previous problem, the magnetic field performed positive work when the conductors were moved apart, whilst the magnetic energy of the currents increased. What energy sources provide the work and the increase in the magnetic energy?

273. What will be the variation in the electric current in the circuit illustrated in Fig. 78 immediately after the switch *K* is closed? The ohmic resistance of the circuit as a whole can be neglected when considering the initial transient state.

274. A condenser of capacity *C* is connected to the upper ends of two parallel vertically mounted copper busbars, spaced a distance *l* apart. A uniform magnetic field *H* acts horizontally at right angles

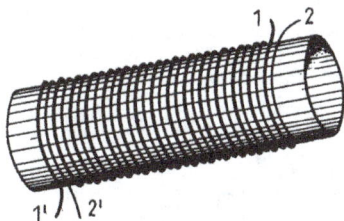

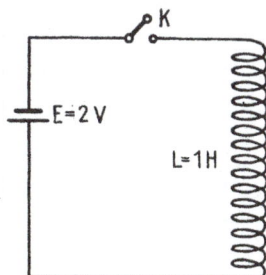

FIG. 77   FIG. 78

to the plane of the busbars. A copper conductor of mass *m* falls with zero initial velocity along the busbars in the magnetic field, in such a way that contact is always maintained between the conductor and the busbars. Neglect the resistance and self-inductance of the conductors, and the friction between the sliding conductor and the busbars. Find: (1) the acceleration of the conductor, (2) the current charging the condenser.

275. The conditions are the same as in the previous problem, except that the condenser is replaced by a solenoid of inductance *L* and negligible resistance. Find the law of motion of the sliding conductor.

276. Two long, parallel, vertical copper busbars, spaced a distance l apart, are connected at the top via a resistance R, and are situated in a uniform magnetic field H, perpendicular to the plane of the busbars. A copper slider of weight P drops without friction along the busbars. What is the steady-state velocity of fall of the slider?

277. A pendulum of length l and mass m, which can be regarded as ideal, consists of a heavy iron ball with a needle at the bottom, suspended by thin wire. The needle is part submerged in mercury contained in a cup (Fig. 79). The point of support A of the pendulum and the mercury are connected via a circuit of resistance R. The pendulum performs small vibrations in a uniform magnetic field H, perpendicular to the plane of vibration. Find the increase in the

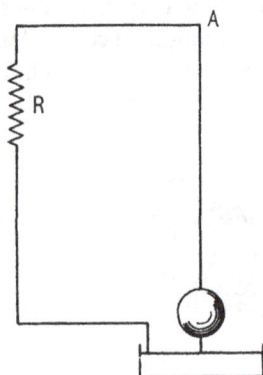

FIG. 79

logarithmic decrement of damping of the pendulum due to the resistance R. The resistance of the medium is proportional to the angular velocity of the pendulum, and the coefficient of proportionality is k.

278. The conditions are the same as in the previous problem, except that the resistance R is replaced by an inductance L. Find the change in the logarithmic decrement and period of vibration.

279. The resistance R of Problem 277 is replaced by a condenser C. Answer the same questions as in 278.

280. A thin copper ring of radius r, mass m and resistance R is suspended from a thread. (1) Find the increase in the logarithmic decrement of the damping of small torsional vibrations of the ring when it is situated in a uniform horizontal magnetic field H, such that the vector H coincides with the plane of the ring in its equilibrium position. (2) Is the answer any different if the ring is situated in a uniform vertical magnetic field? Neglect the inductance of the ring.

281. The copper ring of the previous problem performs torsional vibrations of period T. The inductance of the ring is L, whilst its resistance can be neglected. What change occurs in the period of vibration if the ring is placed in a uniform horizontal magnetic field, the direction of which is perpendicular to the plane of the ring in its equilibrium position?

282. What is the new logarithmic decrement of damping of the ring in the conditions of the previous problem?

283. A rectangular frame of sides a, b lies in the same plane as a straight conductor along which a current I flows; the conductor is parallel to the side b, at a distance $d > a$ from the nearer side. If the frame rotates through 180° about the side b nearer the conductor and remains in this position, what amount of electricity Q passes through any section of the wire of the frame? The wire cross-section is S, the specific resistance of the wire is ϱ.

284. It has been assumed in the previous problem that the frame inductance can be neglected. Is the answer to the problem affected if the inductance cannot be neglected?

285. Instead of rotating through 180°, the frame of Problem 283 rotates continuously with constant velocity. If the resistance of the frame is neglected, but its inductance is taken into account, will the amount of electricity flowing through the frame during the time of a half-rotation now depend on the speed of rotation of the frame?

286. A ballistic galvanometer is connected across a coil wound on a closed magnetised core. The iron plate A which closes the core (Fig. 80) is rapidly removed, when a galvanometer reading of 20 divisions is obtained. The resistance of the coil and galvanometer is 100 ohm. The galvanometer sensitivity is 10^{-8} Coulomb per scale division. What is the change $\Delta\Phi$ in the flux of induction due to the removal of the plate A?

287. How rapidly does the plate A need to be removed from the core of Problem 286, in order for the galvanometer reading to be proportional to the change in the flux?

288. What conditions have to be imposed on the inductance and resistance of the electrical circuit of Problem 286 in order for the galvanometer reading to be proportional to the change in the flux of induction?

289. A frame of area $S = 1400$ cm^2 consists of 100 turns of wire and has a resistance $R = 4\cdot6$ ohm. The frame is mounted in a vertical plane, perpendicular to the plane of the magnetic meridian,

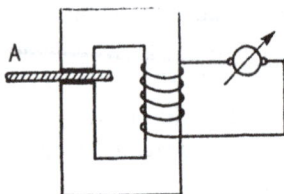

FIG. 80

and is connected to a ballistic galvanometer with a sensitivity $q = 2 \times 10^{-6}$ Coulomb per division. The frame is rotated rapidly about its horizontal diameter through an angle $\alpha = 60°$, so that the plane of the frame becomes parallel to the direction of the earth's magnetic field. What is the reading γ of the galvanometer? The galvanometer resistance $R' = 9\cdot4$ ohm. The strength of the earth's magnetic field is $H = 0\cdot2$ oersted.

290. A non-deformable ring of radius R and small cross-section, made of material whose resistance is vanishingly small (superconductive), is situated in a constant uniform magnetic field of induction B. At the initial instant the plane of the ring is parallel to the direction of the field and the current in the ring is zero. Find the current I in the ring immediately after it has been turned so that its plane is perpendicular to the lines of the magnetic field.

291. Given the conditions of the previous problem, (1) what is the total magnetic flux through the ring after it has been turned? (2) What is the magnitude of the magnetic field-strength at the centre of the ring? (3) Indicate graphically how the field-strength varies along a diameter of the ring.

292. Given the conditions of Problem 290, what is the magnetic field-strength H and the current I in the ring if, after turning it perpendicularly to the external field, the latter is switched off.

293. Find the work A that has to be done in turning the ring in Problem 290.

294. The circuit of Fig. 81 may be used for measuring the mutual inductance between two coils. The resistance R_1 and R_2 and the capacity C of the condenser are selected so that the galvanometer G remains at zero when the switch K in series with the battery E is opened or closed. In this case, what is the mutual inductance M between the coils?

295. In the previous problem, the condenser capacity can be varied in steps of c pF. It turns out that, when the capacity is C, the galvanometer reading is θ to one side, and when the capacity is $C + c$, the reading is θ' to the other side, i.e. a zero reading cannot be obtained. How can the mutual inductance M be determined from these measurements? The galvanometer resistance $R_g \gg R_2$.

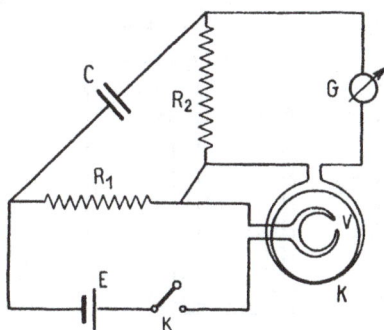

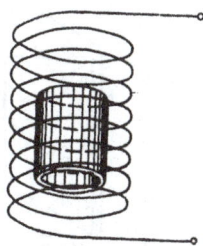

Fig. 81   Fig. 82

296. To remove the gases from the metal parts of vacuum devices, they are burned by eddy currents in the field of a high frequency coil (Fig. 82). A valve anode, consisting of a nickel cylinder of diameter $D = 8$ mm, height $h = 2$ cm, wall thickness $a = 0.1$ mm, is arranged coaxially in a coil of $N = 15$ turns of thick wire, through which a high frequency ($f = 10^5$ c/s) current $I = 50$ amp flows. What is the amount of heat Q supplied per second to the cylinder? The height of the high frequency coil is $H = 10$ cm. Neglect the magnetic field of the eddy currents. The specific resistance of nickel is $\varrho = 7 \times 10^{-6}$ ohm cm.

297. The high coil of the previous problem was used for eddy current heating of a platinum disc of diameter $D = 2$ cm and thickness $a = 0.5$ mm. The disc was mounted at right angles to the coil axis with its centre on the axis. Neglect the magnetic field of the eddy currents. Calculate the amount of heat Q transmitted per second to the disc. The specific resistance of platinum is $\varrho = 10.7 \times 10^{-6}$ ohm cm.

298. To diminish the losses in the iron core of a transformer, the core is made up of thin lamina insulated electrically from one another. Use the following data to find the amount of heat Q transmitted per second to one such lamina: (1) the lamina dimensions are $lab = 20 \times 4 \times 0.01$ cm; (2) the transformer winding has $n = 4$ turns per centimetre length, and carries a 50 c/s current $I = 5$ amp; (3) the permeability of iron is $\mu = 1000$; (4) neglect the magnetic field of the eddy currents. The specific resistance of iron is $\varrho = 9 \times 10^{-6}$ ohm cm.

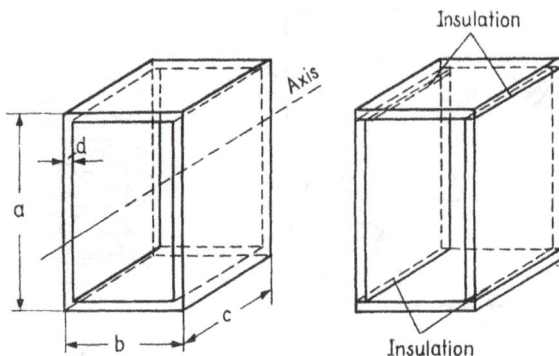

FIG. 83

299. Compare the heat losses W_1 in a metal box, the dimensions of which are shown in Fig. 83, with the losses W_2 in the plates forming the box when the plates are insulated from one another. In both cases the box is situated inside a coil carrying a high frequency current as in Problem 296; the axis of the coil coincides with the axis of the box and is parallel to the side c. The plate thickness d is much less than the dimensions a and b of the box.

300. A coil, of resistance $R = 1$ ohm, inductance L, cross-sectional area $S = 100$ cm², and number of turns $N = 100$, rotates uniformly with angular velocity ω in the earth's magnetic field about a vertical axis passing through the base of the coil perpendicular to its axis (Fig. 84). During rotation the ends of the coil always remain joined to the plates of a plane condenser of capacity C. (1) Find the values of I and V for the stationary state. (2) Find the conditions in which the maximum amount of heat is released in the coil per unit time. (3) Calculate the maximum amount of heat Q released per unit time. The horizontal component of the earth's field is $H = 0.2$ oersted.

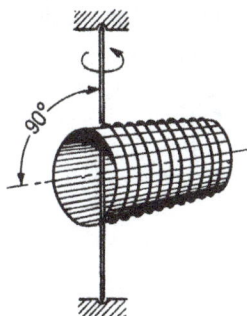

FIG. 84

FIG. 85

301. The coil of the previous problem is stopped suddenly at the instant when the condenser has its maximum charge. (1) What will be the future variation of V if the condition

$$L/C = R^2/4$$

is fulfilled in addition to condition (2) of the previous problem? (2) What will be the amount of heat Q released from the instant of stopping to the vanishing of the current in the circuit?

302. A compass needle of moment of inertia I and magnetic moment M, mounted on a thin vertical axis, performs harmonic vibrations in a horizontal plane (Fig. 85). A horizontally mounted copper disc whose axis coincides with the axis about which the needle vibrates is made to approach the needle from below, and is fixed at a distance such that the motion of the needle becomes aperiodic. The needle is then stopped in its equilibrium position and the disc rotates uniformly about the needle axis with angular velocity ω. (1) What moment M_e must be applied to the needle in order to maintain it in the equilibrium position? (2) What power W will now be liberated in the disc? (3) What is the angular acceleration $\dot{\omega}$ with which the needle starts to move when it is freed? (4) What happens subsequently to the needle if the moment acting on it from the earth's field is comparable in order of magnitude to the moment with which it is acted on by the rotating disc?

303. A sinusoidal voltage $E = E_0 \cos \omega t$ is applied to a cored coil. Determine graphically the form of the current through the winding, given the magnetisation curve of the core material, which possesses hysteresis (Fig. 86). The resistance of the winding can be neglected.

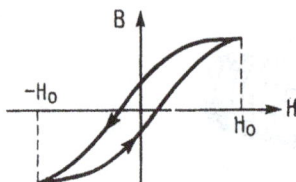

FIG. 86

304. In a Ruhmkorff coil, operating with an interrupter, with a wide spacing between the discharge electrodes connected to the ends of the secondary winding, the spark only jumps in one direction even when the shape of the electrodes is the same. Why?

305. A condenser of capacity C is charged to a potential difference U_0 and discharged through a resistance R. Find the variation with time of the energy W stored in the condenser. Find an analytic expression for the function and draw its graph.

306. A condenser of capacity $C = 1\ \mu F$ discharges through a resistance $R = 1000$ ohm. How long does it take from the start of the discharge for the voltage between the plates to become half its initial value?

307. A condenser of capacity C is charged from a battery of e.m.f. E via a resistance R. Find the variation with time of the power fed to the condenser and draw the graph of the variation.

308. A condenser of capacity C is charged via a resistance R up to a potential equal to the e.m.f. of the battery E. (1) Find the energy Q transformed into heat during the charging. (2) Find the efficiency of the circuit charging the condenser (the useful energy is that stored in the condenser).

309. It was assumed in the previous problem that the initial current, i.e. the current at the instant of closing the switch, was $I_0 = E/R$. Prior to closing the switch the current was zero. Thus the current I_0 must have been established instantaneously after switching on. Is such a jump possible in practice?

310. A condenser is charged from a source of constant e.m.f. E via a resistance R and an inductance L, where

$$R^2 = 4L/C.$$

(1) How does the charge current I vary with time (draw the graph)? (2) Find the time T from the start of the charge at which the current is a maximum. (3) What is the maximum I_{max} of the charge current? (4) What is the voltage V on the condenser at this instant? (5) What is the efficiency η of the circuit?

311. A condenser of capacity C is charged from a battery of e.m.f. E via a resistance R. A neon lamp L is connected in parallel with the condenser (Fig. 87(a)). Figure 87(b) illustrates the idealised

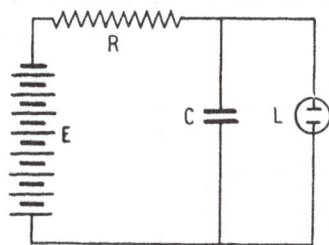

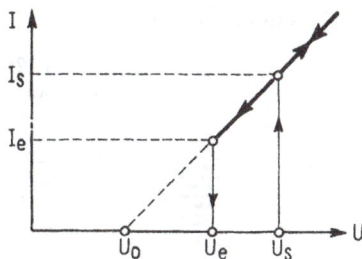

FIG. 87(a)   FIG. 87(b)

characteristic of the lamp. The charging process continues until the potential difference across the condenser plates reaches the value U_s, at which the neon strikes. The condenser then discharges until the potential difference across it falls to the value U_e, at which the neon is extinguished. The charging process then begins again and so on. Draw the graph of the voltage across the condenser as a function of time. Find the charging time t_1 and discharge time t_2 of the condenser, and the period T of the charge/discharge process.

312. Consider the phenomena occurring in the circuit shown in Fig. 88 on closing and opening the knife switch K. Find the voltage V between the points A and B. (Neglect the coil resistance.)

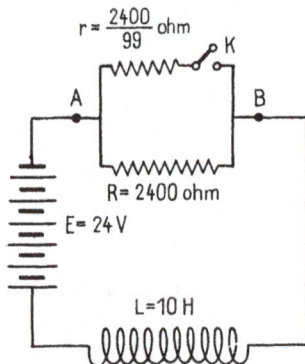

Fig. 88

313. It is well known that the formation of a voltage arc is prevented by shunting a condenser across a knife switch used for interrupting a circuit. To explain the role of the condenser, calculate the voltage V between the points A and B after closing the switch K in the circuit of Fig. 89.

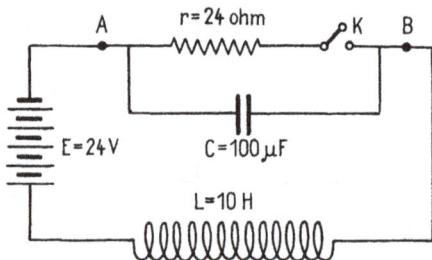

Fig. 89

§ 6. ALTERNATING CURRENTS

314. Using a direct current I, it takes 8 hours to charge an accumulator. In the absence of a d.c. supply, the charging is done from a.c. mains, using a full wave rectifier. In this case an electro-dynamic ammeter installed in the accumulator circuit indicates the same current I. How long does the charging take in these circumstances?

315. A rectifier characteristic is illustrated in Fig. 90. The current is given in ampere, the voltage in volt. The rectifier operates in a push–pull circuit into a purely resistive load of 100 ohm. Find the average current I_{av} through the rectifier–load circuit, if the e.m.f. amplitude is 40 V.

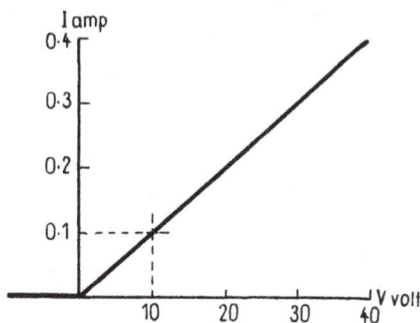

Fig. 90

316. When fed by d.c., an electric furnace requires 5 amp to heat to the necessary temperature. If half-wave rectified a.c. is passed through the furnace element, what must be the reading of (1) a d.c. ammeter, (2) an a.c. ammeter in the circuit in order for the furnace to reach the necessary temperature?

317. The voltmeter of a magneto-electric system connected to a rectifier registers 100 V. What is the maximum value of the voltage supplied by the rectifier if the rectification is (1) half-wave, (2) full-wave?

318. In a rectifier set operating in the so-called Latour circuit (Fig. 91), the a.c. voltage is applied to the points C, D, and the pulsating voltage is taken off from the load resistance R_L (through which the current passes in one direction). What is the relationship of the voltage between A and B with the voltage applied to C, D, if the load resistance is much greater than the impedance of the condensers at the frequency concerned?

319. A heating spiral is fed by a current of 10 amp. What value of the current must be used when calculating the maximum intensity of the magnetic field produced by the current?

320. A 50 c/s circuit includes a rheostat with a resistance $R = 10^3$ ohm and an inductance with a cylindrical iron core and $N = 400$ turns of copper wire. The length of the coil is $l = 40$ cm and its diameter $D = 4$ cm. A phase shift of $\varphi = 30°$ is observed between the e.m.f. and the current. Find the average permeability μ of the core material. Neglect the winding resistance.

321. A 50 c/s circuit contains a rheostat with a resistance of $R = 100$ ohm, a coil with inductance $L = 1$ H and a condenser of capacity $C = 1\ \mu$F. What is the phase shift φ between the current and the voltage across the circuit, and what is its direction?

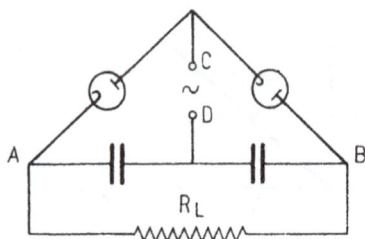

FIG. 91

322. A 50 c/s circuit contains a rheostat and a coil of inductance $L = 0.1$ H. The phase shift between the voltage and the current is found to be $\varphi = 30°$. What is the resistance R of the rheostat and what capacity C must be put in series with it in order to eliminate the phase shift?

323. A condenser filled with liquid dielectric possessing conductivity is equivalent to a capacity C shunted by a resistance R. What phase displacement between the voltage and current is produced when such a condenser is connected in an a.c. circuit of frequency ω?

324. A shorted turn of wire with inductance L and resistance R rotates uniformly with angular velocity ω about an axis in the plane of the wire, in a uniform magnetic field whose direction is perpendicular to the axis of rotation. What is the angle α between the direction of the field and the plane of the wire when the current in the wire is maximum?

325. A square frame rotates uniformly with angular velocity ω in a uniform magnetic field perpendicular to the axis of rotation

(Fig. 92). The ends of the frame are connected to a coil L. The resistance of the circuit is negligible. In what position of the frame is the current in it a maximum?

326. If the coil in the previous problem is replaced by a condenser C in series with a resistance R, what is the position of the frame for the current in it to be a maximum?

327. A coil of inductance L is connected in series with the condenser of Problem 323 in an a.c. circuit. As a result, the phase displacement between the voltage and current becomes zero. What is the resistance of the condenser dielectric?

328. A coil of inductance $L = 0\cdot3$ H and resistance $R = 100$ ohm is connected in a 50 c/s a.c. circuit with an r.m.s. voltage $V = 120$ V. Find the current amplitude I, the phase difference φ between the current and the voltage, and the power W produced in the circuit.

329. The following three-voltmeter method is sometimes used for determining the power liberated by a.c. in a coil of inductance L,

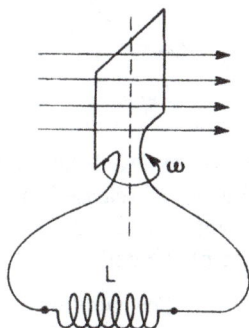

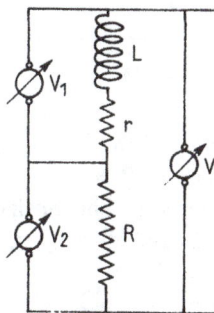

FIG. 92   FIG. 93

resistance r. A known resistance R is connected in series with the coil, and the three voltmeters are connected as shown in Fig. 93. The meter V_1 measures the r.m.s. voltage across the coil, V_2 the voltage across the resistance R, and V the voltage between the ends of the circuit. Find the required power W.

330. The following method is sometimes used for measuring the power liberated by a.c. in a coil of inductance L and resistance r. A known resistance R is connected in parallel with the coil, and three ammeters are connected as shown in Fig. 94. The meter I_1 measures the r.m.s. current in the coil, I_2 the current through the resistance R and I the total current. Find the required power W from the meter readings.

331. A coil of 40 cm diameter whose axis lies in a horizontal plane is composed of $N = 1000$ turns of fine copper wire of cross-section $S = 0.1$ mm^2. The coil rotates in the earth's magnetic field about a vertical axis through its centre, at a rate of $n = 10^3$ r.p.m.

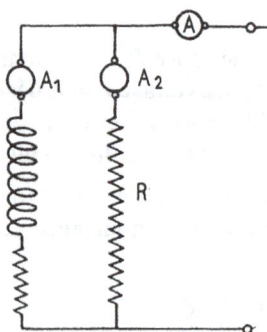

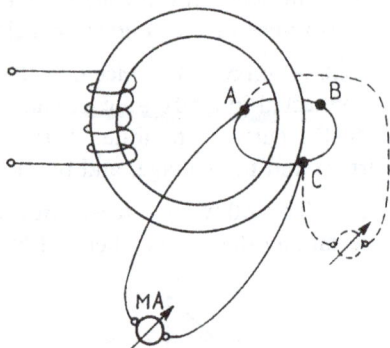

FIG. 94   FIG. 95

The ends of the coil remain joined to an external circuit whose resistance is $R = 154$ ohm. Find the power W released in the external circuit. The horizontal component of the earth's field is $H = 0.2$ oersted. Neglect the inductance of the coil.

332. An iron core carries two windings. The winding with the greater number of turns N is connected to a source of sinusoidal e.m.f. E volts. The other winding has one turn of resistance R. The points A, B, C of the turn are at equal distances from one another (Fig. 95). (1) If a sensitive a.c. ammeter of resistance r is joined between two of these points, what will it indicate? (2) What is the change in its reading if it is moved to the position indicated by a dotted line in the sketch? The iron core has no magnetic leakage. The inductance of the turn and the connecting leads can be neglected.

333. If the resistance of the turn in the previous problem is negligible, what determines the current in the turn?

334. What is the total impedance (to a.c. of frequency ω) of a network consisting of a capacity C in parallel with a resistance R?

335. We are given two independent circuits. The first consists of a source of e.m.f. of given frequency in series with a coil of inductance L and a resistance R. The second consists of a source of e.m.f. of the same frequency and a condenser of capacity C shunted by a resistance R. What is the relationship between L, C, R if the phase difference between the voltage and current has the same absolute value in both circuits.

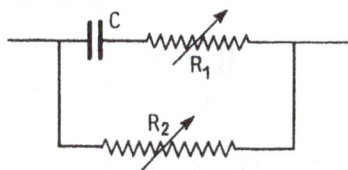

FIG. 96

336. Given the circuit of Fig. 96, how is the phase difference between the currents in the branches affected if (1) the resistance R_2 is varied, (2) R_1 is varied?

337. In the circuit of Fig. 97, we are given L, C, R and

$$I_2 = I_0 \cos \omega t.$$

Find E, I_1 and the phase difference φ between E and the voltage V across the condenser.

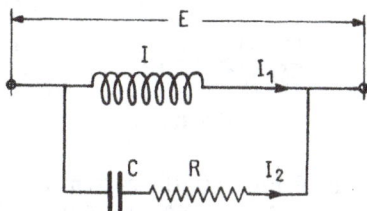

FIG. 97

338. Find the total impedance r of the circuit illustrated in Fig. 98. The circular frequency of the a.c. in the circuit is ω. Find the conditions in which the circuit impedance is a maximum, if $R \ll L\omega$, and find this maximum impedance r_{max}.

339. Why is short-circuiting a condenser equivalent to its capacity becoming infinitely large?

340. The input voltage to the filter of Fig. 99 is given as

$$U_1 = (120 \sin 300t + 120 \sin 600t) \text{ V.}*$$

Find the output voltage U_2 as a function of time.

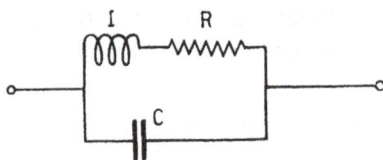

FIG. 98

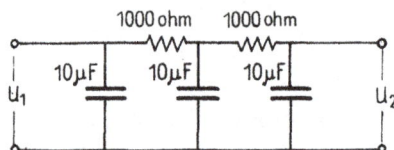

FIG. 99

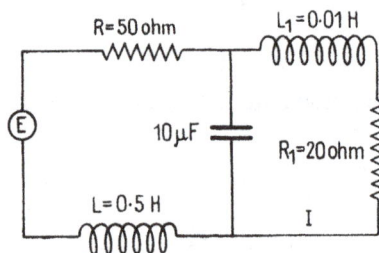

FIG. 100

341. In the circuit of Fig. 100, the current in the coil L_1 of the oscillatory circuit is $I = 0.5 \cos 600t$. Find the e.m.f. E.

* Here, and in many subsequent problems, the argument of the sine or cosine is a number multiplied by t. The dimension of the number is the reciprocal of time (i.e. the number has the dimensions of a frequency) and the number is expressed in $\sec^{-1}$. Thus the product of the number with time is a dimensionless quantity. To avoid complexity in the formulae, neither the units in which the number is measured, nor the units of time, are indicated.

342. Show that a transformer with windings of negligible resistance and without leakage (Fig. 101(a)), operating into a purely resistive load, is equivalent as regards its input impedance to the circuit of Fig. 101(b) (n is the transformer ratio).

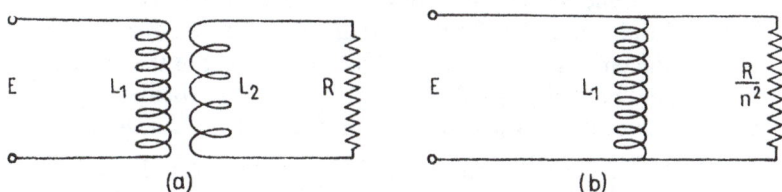

(a)   (b)

FIG. 101

343. For the a.c. circuit illustrated in Fig. 102, find (1) the phase difference between the voltage across the condenser and the current through the resistance R; (2) the phase difference between the current through the condenser and the current through the resistance

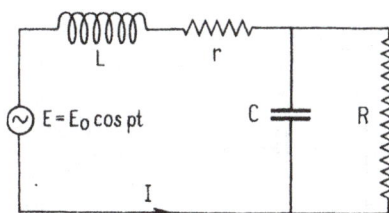

FIG. 102

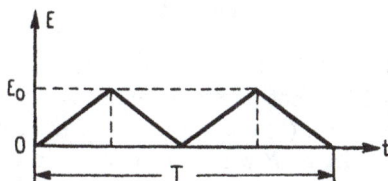

FIG. 103

R; (3) the phase difference between the voltage across the resistance R and the e.m.f. E applied to the circuit.

344. A periodic voltage has the shape shown in Fig. 103. Find its effective (r.m.s.) value E_{eff}.

345. The shape of the current through an induction coil is similar to that shown in Fig. 103. The peak value of the current is I_0. What is the voltage drop across the coil? Draw a graph showing the variation of the drop over a period.

346. A condenser of capacity $C = 0.025 \ \mu F$ is charged up to a potential difference $V = 20$ V and is discharged through a conductor of inductance $L = 4 \ \mu H$. The resistance present in the circuit is $r = 1$ ohm. Find the circular frequency ω of the oscillation, the logarithmic decrement θ and the peak value of the current I_0.

347. A circuit consisting of a coil ($L = 0.2$ H, $R = 10$ ohm) in series with a condenser C is connected across a.c. mains ($f = 50 \ sec^{-1}$, voltage amplitude $E_0 = 100$ V). Find C so that the voltage V across the coil is a maximum and determine this maximum.

348. What is the capacity C in the previous problem if the current amplitude in the circuit is 1 amp?

349. What is the capacity C in Problem 347 if the amplitude of the voltage across the resistance is 0.1 V?

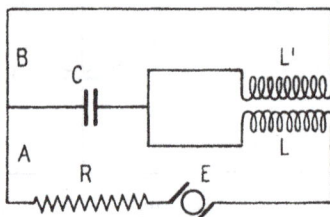

FIG. 104

350. Given the circuit of Fig. 104, find (1) the frequency of the e.m.f. E for which current passes in circuit A whilst the current in circuit B remains zero, (2) the frequency of the e.m.f. E for which current passes in circuit B whilst the current in circuit A remains zero. The mutual inductance between the two circuits is $M \neq L$.

351. In the circuit of the previous problem, $L = L' = 2M = 0.01$ H, $C = 1 \ \mu F$ and $R = 100$ ohm. Find the amplitudes I_0 and I_0' of the currents in circuits A and B in cases (1) and (2) of the previous problem if the peak value of the e.m.f. E is 100 V; calculate the power W delivered by the source of e.m.f. in these two cases.

352. In the circuit of Fig. 105, the capacity C can be varied continuously within wide limits. The e.m.f. of the source is $E_0 \cos \omega t$. Find the power delivered by the source as a function of the capacity C. For what value of C is this power a maximum? Find the maximum.

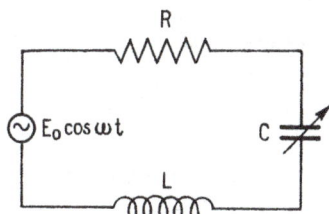

FIG. 105

353. A generator delivers energy over a line into a load. The generator r.m.s. voltage is E. The resistance and inductance of the line plus generator are R_0, L_0 respectively. The resistance and inductance of the load are R and L. Find (1) the power W delivered by the source, (2) the useful power W', (3) the efficiency η' of the circuit.

354. Find the power W delivered by the source, the useful power W' and the efficiency η for the circuit shown in Fig. 106; the source e.m.f. is $E_0 \cos \omega t$.

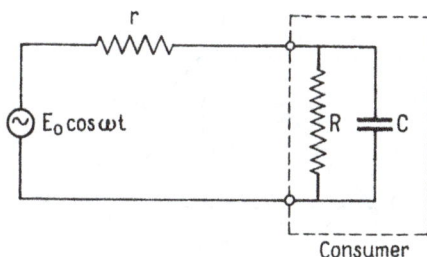

FIG. 106

355. Figure 107(a) illustrates an electrical circuit. The amplitudes of the voltage, current and phase shift between the voltage and current in the load are illustrated in Fig. 107(b). Find the e.m.f. E of the source and the efficiency η of the circuit. What would the efficiency η' be if, with the same amplitudes of voltage and current, the load possessed only pure resistance?

356. The real and wattless components of the current in a load are equal. The amplitude of the voltage across the input terminals of the load is $V = 100$ V, whilst the current amplitude is $I = 10$ amp. Find the amplitude of the source e.m.f. if the resistance of the line plus source is $R_0 = 5$ ohm.

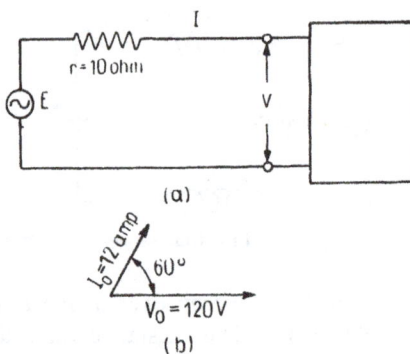

(a)

(b)

FIG. 107

357. How can an a.c. ammeter and a.c. voltmeter be used for measuring a capacity C? Give the circuit and relevant formulae.

358. A condenser is connected in series with a meter, which reads 240 m amp, across 120 V 50 c/s a.c. mains. What is the capacity

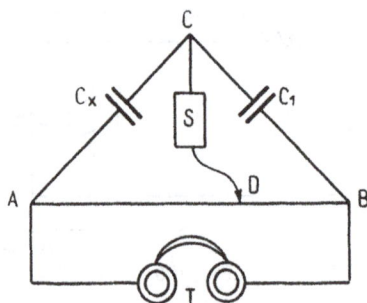

FIG. 108

C of the condenser? The resistance of the meter and connecting leads can be neglected.

359. In what conditions can the method described in the previous problem be used for measuring the capacity of a condenser?

360. What is a simple way of determining the capacity of a condenser possessing leakage, using the method of Problem 357.

361. The bridge method illustrated in Fig. 108 is sometimes used for measuring the capacity of a condenser. AB is a slide wire, S is an audio-frequency generator, T is a headphone, C_x is the condenser to be measured, C_1 is a calibrated condenser. Obtain the balance conditions (i.e. the conditions in which there is no sound in the headphone). Is it possible to interchange the generator and the headphone in the bridge circuit?

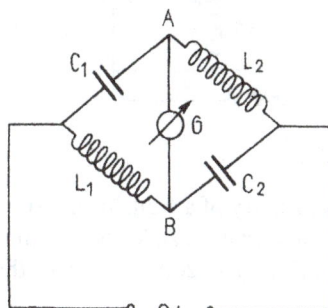 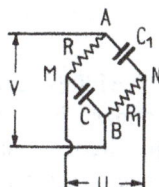

FIG. 109   FIG. 110

362. Figure 109 illustrates a bridge circuit. Is it possible to obtain absence of current through the a.c. meter G whatever the ratio of L and C?

363. A voltage $V = V_0 \sin \omega t$ is applied to the points A and B of the circuit shown in Fig. 110, whilst the voltage $U = U_0 \sin(\omega t - \varphi)$ is taken off from the points M, N. Show that $V_0 = U_0$ when $R_1 C_1 = RC$, and find the phase shift φ. (2) What is the value of φ if

$$R = 1/\omega C?$$

(This circuit is one of the simplest types of phase-shifter.)

364. In the circuit of Fig. 111 (with the values as shown) $E = 150 \cos 300t$ V. Find the value of the capacity C such that the current through the milliammeter A is 5 mamp.

365. Find the inductance L of the choke in the circuit of Fig. 112 such that the voltage amplitude U_2 at the filter output is one tenth the amplitude U_1 at the input. The frequency is 100 c/s.

366. A step-down transformer is used for feeding an electric bell. The transformer primary is generally left connected across the mains (Fig. 113). Is the customer paying all the time for the primary being connected across the mains or does he only pay for the brief periods when the button is pressed? Why is it to be preferred to connect the button in the secondary side of the transformer?

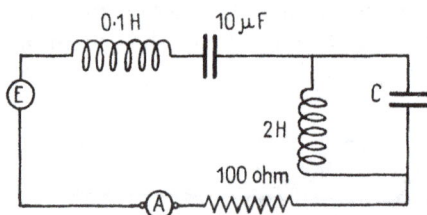

Fig. 111

367. The idling current in the primary of a transformer (i.e. when the secondary is open circuit) fed from 220 V, 50 c/s mains, is 0·1 amp. The resistance of the primary is 200 ohm. Find the self-inductance of the primary.

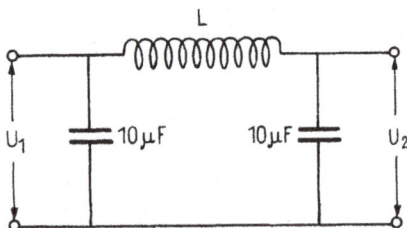

Fig. 112

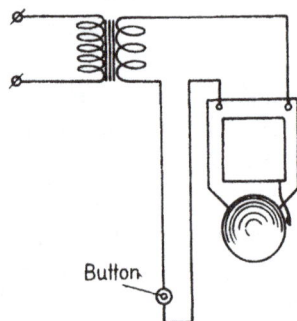

Fig. 113

368. A transformer for stepping up the voltage from 100 V to 3300 V has a closed ring-type core. A wire is passed through the ring and its ends are connected to a voltmeter (Fig. 114). The voltmeter reads 0·5 V. How many turns have the transformer windings?

369. A transformer core is in the form of a square-section (side $a = 10$ cm) torus. The distance from the axis of the torus to the centre of its cross-section is $d = 25$ cm. The primary and secondary windings have $N_1 = 500$ and $N_2 = 10,000$ turns respectively. The secondary is open circuit. The ends of the primary are connected to a generator and a sinusoidal current of circular frequency $\omega = 314 \sec^{-1}$ and effective value $I = 1\cdot4$ amp flows through the circuit. Find (1) the self-inductance L of the primary winding, (2) the amplitude of the voltage V obtained across the ends of the secondary. The resistance of the primary winding is $r = 0\cdot5$ ohm; the susceptibility of the core material is $\varkappa = 12$.

370. A plate condenser is connected across a d.c. battery circuit. The distance between the plates varies in accordance with the

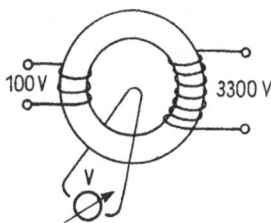

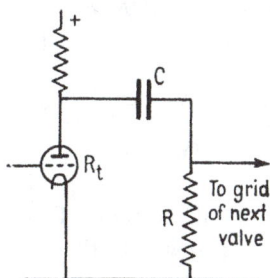

FIG. 114   FIG. 115

harmonic law $d = d_0(1 + a \cos \omega t)$, where $a \ll 1$. What is the current I flowing in the circuit if the battery e.m.f. is E, and the plate area is S? The resistance of the circuit can be neglected since it is much less than $1/C\omega$.

371. The oscillatory voltage on the anode of an amplifier valve is fed to the grid circuit of the next valve via a "blocking condenser" C (Fig. 115), which protects the grid circuit from the d.c. anode voltage. In order for the electrons arriving at the grid of the next valve to be able to return to the cathode, a resistance R ("grid leak") is connected between cathode and grid. Calculate the minimum capacity C of the blocking condenser if $R = 1$ M ohm, the amplifier is designed for frequencies from 5×10^5 to 15×10^5 c/s and the voltage loss in the condenser must not exceed $0\cdot1$ per cent throughout the frequency range.

372. The condenser C in the circuit of Fig. 116 is arranged to pass only the a.c. component V_2 of the input voltage V_1. Find the

least value of this condenser from the condition that the voltage
drop must not exceed 5 per cent in the frequency range 50 to
10,000 c/s. The resistance $R = 0.5$ M ohm.

373. A 50 c/s voltage is applied to the deflector plates of a cathode
ray tube via the circuit shown in Fig. 117. The capacity C of the
condenser is $0.5 \, \mu F$. Find the resistance R such that we see on the
screen of the tube (1) a circle, (2) an ellipse in which one axis has
twice the length of other.

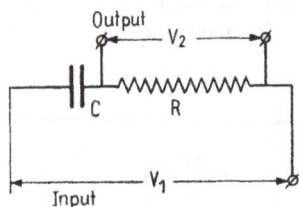

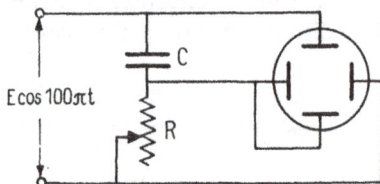

FIG. 116   FIG. 117

374. Find the ratio of the major semi-axis of the ellipse in the
previous problem to the radius of the circle.

375. The phase difference between two points can be found by
using a cathode ray tube in the circuit of Fig. 118. (1) How is the
measurement carried out? (2) Can the sign of the phase shift be
found by this method?

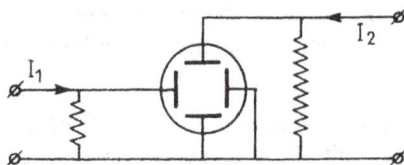

FIG. 118

376. The answer to the previous problem gives a method of finding the phase shift between two points. This method is not sufficiently accurate. The phase shift can be found more accurately
from the position of the principal axes of the ellipse. Find an expression for the phase shift in terms of the lengths and slopes of the
semi-axes of the ellipse.

377. By using the cathode ray oscilloscope circuit of Fig. 119, it is
possible in principle to measure the power absorbed in the (R, L, r)

circuit. How is the measurement performed? What data are required for the measurement?

378. In the circuit illustrated in Fig. 120 (a) (delta connection), we are given the voltages between the points 1, 2, 3 and the

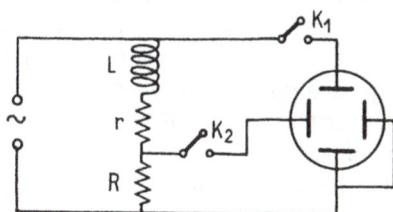

FIG. 119

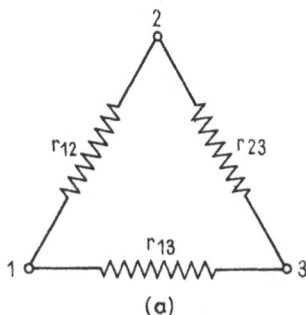

(a)

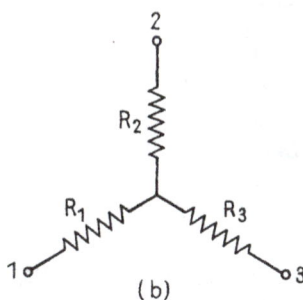

(b)

FIG. 120

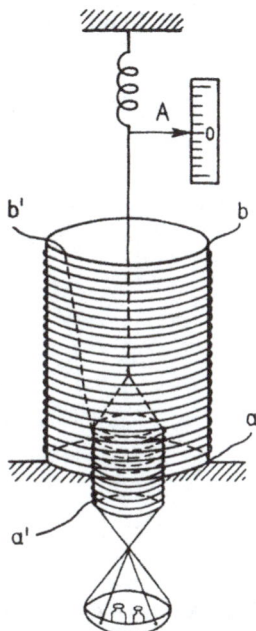

FIG. 121

resistances r_{12}, r_{23} and r_{13}. Find the resistances R_1, R_2, R_3 in the branches of the "equivalent" circuit of Fig. 120 (b) (star connection). (The "equivalence" condition amounts to the fact that, given the same voltage drop between each pair of points 1, 2, 3 in both circuits, the same currents flow through these points.)

379. Figure 121 shows the schematic arrangement of an electro-dynamometer. The device consists of a fixed coil (terminals a, b) mounted vertically. A second coil (terminals a', b') is suspended coaxially with the first from a spring and has a pan with small weights attached to it. If the ends b, b' of the coils are joined, and a current of I amp passed through from a to a', 20 g has to be added to the pan in order for the position of the coil to remain unchanged, i.e. for the indicator needle A to remain at the zero position. Find the load p that has to be added to the pan for the position of the coil to be unchanged if a 2 amp 50 c/s a.c. current passes through the circuit ab, whilst a current of 0·5 amp of the same frequency, with a phase shift of 30° relative to the first current, passes through the circuit $a'b'$.

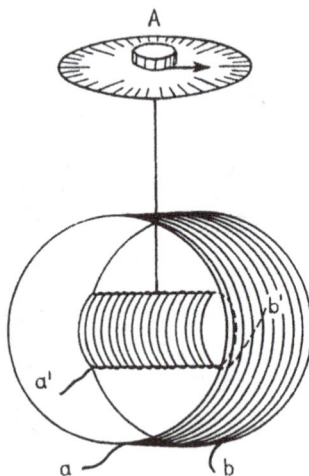

Fig. 122

380. A device consists of two mutually perpendicular coils, one of which (the outer) is held fixed, whilst the second is suspended from a thread inside the first (Fig. 122). The end b of the first coil is joined to a' and a 50 c/s current I_1 passed through both coils, as a result of which the inner coil rotates. This coil is returned to its original position (perpendicular to the fixed coil) by a rotation to the left of the knob A through α_1 divisions. When another 50 c/s current I_2 is passed, a rotation of A to the left through α_2 divisions is required to bring the coil to its original position. Finally, the current I_1 is passed through the first coil from a to b, and the current I_2 through the second from a' to b'; the knob A now has to be turned α_3 divisions to the right to bring the coil to its original position. Assuming that the twisting angle of the thread is proportional to the moment, find the phase shift between the currents I_1 and I_2, if $\alpha_1 = 14°5'$; $\alpha_2 = 10°$; $\alpha_3 = 6°$.

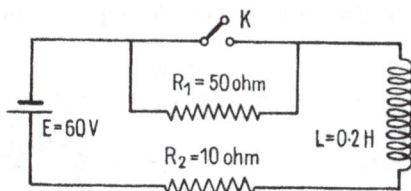

FIG. 123

381. How are the twisting angles of the thread of the previous problem affected in all the experiments if (1) the ends of the two coils are interchanged, (2) the ends of only one of the coils are interchanged? (3) Can the device be used to find the sign of the phase difference of I_2 with respect to I_1?

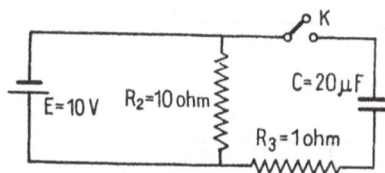

FIG. 124

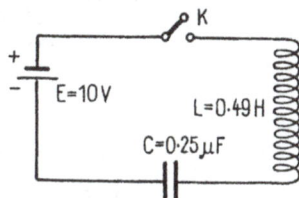

FIG. 125

382. Find the current I in the circuit of Fig. 123 as a function of time after closing the switch K.

383. Find the law of variation of the current I through the battery E after closing the switch K in the circuit of Fig. 124; draw the graph of the current variation after closing the switch.

384. An electrical circuit consists of a battery, condenser and coil (Fig. 125). Find the current I in the circuit as a function of time, assuming that the switch is closed at the instant $t = 0$. The component values are shown in the sketch. Neglect the internal resistance of the battery and the resistance of the rest of the circuit.

385. Find the variation of the voltage V across the condenser C after closing the switch K in the circuit of Fig. 126.

386. In the circuit shown in Fig. 127, find the voltage V across the condenser C as a function of time, after closing the switch K at the instant $t = 0$.

387. For the circuit of Fig. 128, find the charge q on the condenser C as a function of time after closing the switch K.

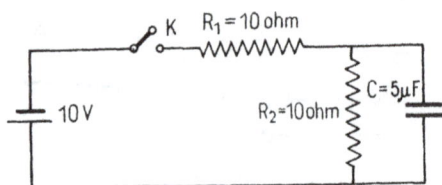

FIG. 126

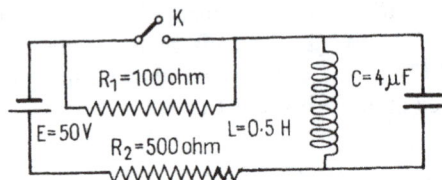

FIG. 127

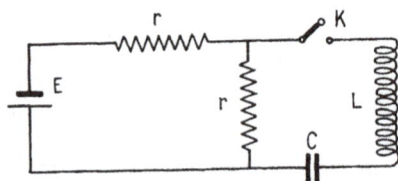

FIG. 128

388. For the circuit of Fig. 129, find the variation (with time) of the current I through the coil after closing the switch K. The component values are as shown.

389. The battery in the circuit of Problem 383 is replaced by a source of sinusoidal e.m.f. of frequency 10 c/s. The switch K is closed at the instant when the e.m.f. reaches its peak value. The amplitude of the e.m.f. is 10 V. Find the voltage across the condenser as a function of time.

390. A source of sinusoidal e.m.f. ($E = 100 \sin 100\,\pi t$ V) is switched across a coil of inductance $L = 1$ H at the instant $t = 0$ (Fig. 130). Find the current I in the circuit. (Neglect the internal resistance of the source and the resistance of the coil and connecting leads.)

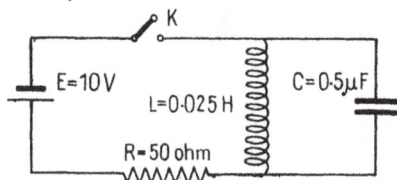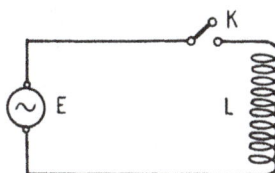

FIG. 129   FIG. 130

391. The switch K is closed at the instant $t = 0$ in the circuit of Fig. 131. Find the current through the resistance and the voltage across the condenser. The amplitude of the e.m.f. is $E_0 = 100$ V, its frequency is $\omega = 200\pi\,\sec^{-1}$, the remaining values being as shown on the sketch. (Neglect the internal resistance of the source.)

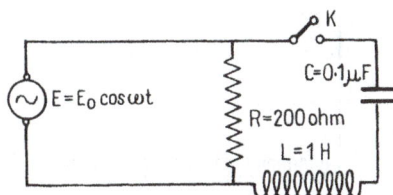

FIG. 131

392. The switch K is closed at the instant $t = 0$ in the circuit of Fig. 132. Find the voltage drop V across the resistance as a function of time. We are given $E_0 = 100$ V, $\omega = 100\,\pi\,\sec^{-1}$; the component values are shown in the sketch. (Neglect the internal resistance of the source.)

393. In the circuit of Fig. 133, find the current I through the resistance R_1 after closing the switch K at the instant $t = 0$. The amplitude of the e.m.f. is 100 V, the frequency $100\,\pi\,\sec^{-1}$. The component values are shown in the sketch. (Neglect the internal resistance of the source.)

394. Two identical condensers C are connected in series with a coil of inductance L (Fig. 134). With the switch K open, one of the condensers is charged to a potential difference V. The source is then taken out of circuit. Find the variation with time of the charges on the condensers after closing the switch K.

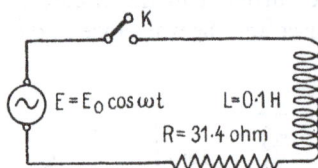

FIG. 132

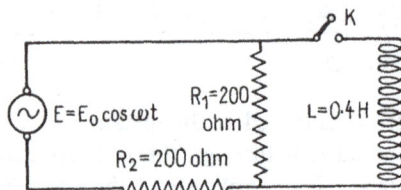

FIG. 133

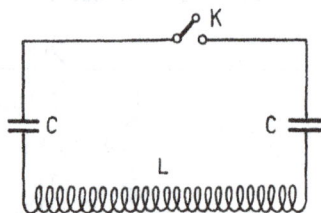

FIG. 134

395. Find the inductance L of a coil which, when connected in parallel with a condenser of capacity $C = 10\ \mu F$, forms a circuit resonating at 50 c/s.

396. An oscillatory circuit consists of a coil of length $l = 40$ cm, diameter $d = 4$ cm, close wound with wire whose thickness, including the insulation, is $a = 1$ mm, and a set of 10 plate condensers connected in parallel, the plate dimensions of which are $m \times n = 20 \times 15$ cm^2, whilst the plate separation is by a layer of dielectric of thickness $D = 0.1$ mm and dielectric constant $\varepsilon = 5$. Find approximately the natural period T of the circuit.

397. What is the wavelength λ of the electromagnetic wave corresponding to the natural frequency of oscillation of a circuit consisting of a coil of inductance $L = 0.4$ H shunted by a capacity $C = \frac{1}{90} \mu F$?

398. What capacity C is required to make a coil of inductance $L = 25 \mu H$ resonate at a wavelength $\lambda = 100$ m?

399. Find the relationship between the amplitude of the current I_0 and voltage V_0 for the free oscillations of a circuit consisting of a coil of inductance L and a condenser of capacity C.

400. An external e.m.f. of amplitude 10 V is applied to an oscillatory circuit consisting of a condenser of capacity $C = 0.1 \mu F$, a coil of inductance $L = 0.01$ H and a resistance $R = 10$ ohm joined in series. What is the frequency f of the e.m.f., connected in series with the circuit, if the amplitude of the current through the circuit is known to be 1 amp?

401. An external periodic e.m.f. of constant amplitude acts on an oscillatory circuit with natural frequency ω_0 and logarithmic decrement $\vartheta = 0.02$. The frequency ω of the external e.m.f. is at first equal to ω_0, then is varied so that the power dissipated in the circuit falls to a half. Find the change in frequency as a percentage of the natural (or resonant) frequency ω_0.

402. An oscillatory circuit includes a coil of inductance L and a resistance R. It is desired to replace the coil by two coils of inductances L_1, L_2 and resistances R_1, R_2. What conditions must these coil values satisfy in order for the period and damping of the natural oscillations in the circuit to remain unchanged? Consider the cases of series and parallel connection of the coils (regard the mutual inductance between the coils as zero).

403. If the local mains supply is used as an aerial, a blocking condenser has to be fitted between the mains and the receiver. Why is this done, and what must be the capacity of the condenser?

404. An oscillatory circuit consists of a condenser and a coil of inductance $L = 1$ H. What is the resistance of the circuit if the amplitude of the natural oscillations in it is known to decrease by the factor $e = 2.7$ after 0.05 sec.

405. How many periods are needed for the amplitude of the oscillations in a circuit in which $L = 1$ H, $C = 0.5 \mu F$, $R = 30$ ohm to diminish by a factor $e = 2.7$?

406. What is characterised by the damping factor

$$\delta = R/2L$$

of a circuit? What is characterised by the logarithmic decrement

$$\vartheta = \pi R \sqrt{C/L}$$

of a circuit?

407. An oscillatory circuit has the following values: $L = 40\,\mu\text{H}$, $C = 270\,\text{pF}$, $R = 8\,\text{ohm}$. Find the time required for the amplitude of its natural oscillations to diminish e^2 times.

408. A device used in radio engineering is a variometer, the inductance of which can be varied within known limits. Figure 135 illustrates one type of variometer circuit. A coil B is mounted inside a coil A and can be rotated about an axis perpendicular to the axes of both coils. The inductance of coil A is $1000\,\mu\text{H}$, and of coil B $400\,\mu\text{H}$. The maximum mutual inductance between the two coils is $500\,\mu\text{H}$. Find the maximum and minimum inductance of the variometer when its coils are connected in series, i.e. the inductance of the circuit between a and b.

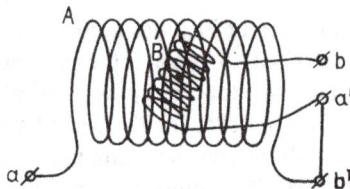

FIG. 135

409. Given two coils with fixed mutual orientation and an inductance bridge, how can the mutual inductance between the coils be determined?

410. A source of sinusoidal e.m.f. of constant amplitude is connected in series with an oscillatory circuit. Estimate approximately the e.m.f. across the coil and the voltage across the capacity in the case of very small and very large frequencies (by comparison with the natural frequency of the circuit), neglecting the internal resistance of the source.

411. An external e.m.f. E is applied to an oscillatory circuit (Fig. 136). Find the current I and the phase difference φ between I and E at resonance.

412. A source of sinusoidal e.m.f. of constant amplitude and variable frequency is connected in series with a series combination of resistance R, inductance L and capacity C. The source frequency is varied till it is tuned to the resonant frequency of the circuit, then the capacity C is halved and the source again tuned to resonance. Does the current at resonance alter? What is the ratio of the resonant frequencies corresponding to the two cases?

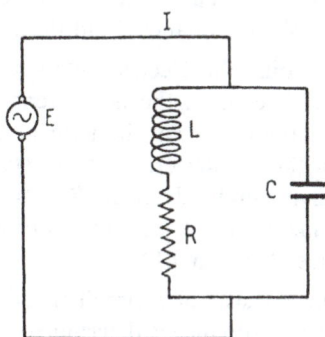

FIG. 136

413. What is the change in the power dissipated by the source at resonance in Problem 411 if the circuit inductance is doubled and the capacity halved, whilst $L\omega \gg R$? The frequency and amplitude of the e.m.f. remain constant throughout.

414. Show that, in the circuit of Problem 412, the current amplitude I when the frequency of the external e.m.f. deviates by the small amount Δf* from the resonant frequency f_0 is connected with the current amplitude I_0 at resonance by

$$I = I_0/\sqrt{1 + (2\Delta f/f_0)^2 Q^2}$$

where $Q = (1/R)\sqrt{L/C}$ is the "Q" of the circuit.

415. In an oscillatory circuit consisting of a variometer and condenser, the capacity was doubled then the variometer inductance

* Δf is termed the "detuning", and $\Delta f/f_0$ the "relative detuning".

readjusted to obtain resonance at the previous frequency. How are the following affected: (1) the logarithmic decrement of the circuit, (2) the damping factor, (3) the current at resonance and (4) the voltage across the condenser at resonance, assuming that in both cases an e.m.f. of the same amplitude is applied in series with the circuit, and that the resistance of the variometer remains unchanged?

416. Find the Q of a circuit from the following data: the resonant frequency $f_{res} = 600$ kc/s, the capacity $C = 350$ pF, the resistive component for frequencies close to resonance is $R = 15$ ohm.

417. A source of e.m.f. of amplitude $E_0 = 5$ V is connected in series with an oscillatory circuit. The amplitude of the voltage on the condenser is 150 V at resonance. Find the Q of the circuit.

418. At a given point the electric field-strength produced by a radio station A is five times the field-strength from station B. Find the Q of the circuit that can be used at the given point to receive station B without interference from station A, if this requires that the signal amplitude from B in the circuit is at least 10 times the amplitude from A. The frequency of station A is 210 kc/s and of B 200 kc/s (see Problem 414).

419. A wavemeter consists of a circuit tuned to resonance with an external e.m.f. The resonance is determined from the maximum of the current in the circuit by using a device whose accuracy is 2 per cent. The circuit data are the same as in Problem 416. Calculate the percentage accuracy of frequency measurement by the wavemeter.

420. A two-wire line is made of ideal conductors (without heat losses). One pair of ends of the line is connected to a constant current generator, the other to an impedance (load). Show that, if the voltage drop in the wires is neglected, the energy flux vector S (Poynting vector) in the space between the wires is directed along the wires from the generator to the load. How is the situation affected if the resistance of the wires is taken into account?

421. The two-wire line of the previous problem is connected at one end to a sinusoidal current generator. The voltage and current in the line are in phase. Show that the Poynting vector in the space between the wires is always directed from the generator to the load.

422. In the line of the previous problem the current remains 90° out of phase with the voltage. Show that the Poynting vector reverses its direction every quarter period, so that the energy flux per period is zero (standing wave).

423. Direct current flows along a straight wire possessing resistance; (1) find, for an arbitrary point on the lateral surface of the wire, the direction of the component of the Poynting vector S due to the tangential component of E; (2) show that the product of the Poynting vector with the magnitude of the lateral surface of the wire is equal to the power produced by the current in the wire.

424. Find the displacement current density j_c in a plate condenser, the plates of which move apart with velocity u whilst remaining parallel, if (1) the charge ϱ on the plates remains constant; (2) the potential difference V between the plates remains constant. The distance d between the plates always remains small compared with their length and breadth; (2) what change occurs if the plates move closer instead of moving apart?

§ 7. ELECTRIC CURRENTS IN LIQUIDS

425. A cylindrical electrolytic bath containing a solution of copper sulphate between cylindrical copper electrodes is mounted above the north pole of a strong electromagnet (Fig. 137), the

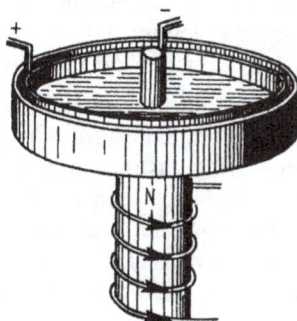

FIG. 137

electrodes being connected to the poles of a battery. What happens to the electrolyte in these circumstances?

426. A 1 amp current passes through an electrolyte. Supposing for simplicity that the mobilities of the ions are the same, it can be assumed that the positive ions carry positive charge of $\frac{1}{2}$ Coulomb in one direction per second, the negative ions negative charge of $\frac{1}{2}$ Coulomb in the opposite direction. What does the amount of material deposited on the electrodes correspond to in this case: to $\frac{1}{2}$ Coulomb at the anode and $\frac{1}{2}$ Coulomb at the cathode, or to 1 Coulomb at the anode and 1 Coulomb at the cathode?

427. How many ampere-hours are required to deposit on the electrode of a galvanic cell a gram-equivalent of substance?

428. Use the laws of electrolysis to determine the ratio e/m_H of the charge to the mass of a hydrogen ion.

429. By using the laws of electrolysis and Avogadro's number, find the mass of a hydrogen ion m_H and the charge e of an electron. Avogadro's number $\approx 6 \cdot 02 \times 10^{23}$.

430. A battery of galvanic cells (e.m.f. $E = 0 \cdot 9$ V, internal resistance $\varrho = 0 \cdot 6$ ohm) consists of 30 individual cells connected in three identical parallel groups. What is the amount of copper depositing at the cathode during 5 min operation of the battery, connected to a load whose resistance is 205 ohm. The atomic weight of copper is $63 \cdot 57$.

431. On passing current through a voltmeter containing acidified water, 150 cm^3 fire-damp forms in the course of 3 min, and the water level in the voltmeter falls 12 cm. The atmospheric pressure at the time of the experiment is 750 mm Hg, and the specific weight of the acidified water is $1 \cdot 13$ gcm^{-3}. Find the current I.

432. Current is passed from an accumulator battery through a jar containing acidified water. During discharge of the battery a certain amount of detonating gas is obtained, such that, when it is burnt, 35 per cent of the energy used in charging the battery is obtained. If, instead of a single jar, a number of jars is connected in series, a greater time will obviously be needed for the same amount of electricity to flow as in the case of one jar. But, by Faraday's law, the amount of substance deposited depends only on the amount of electricity flowing through the electrolyte. Thus the same amount of detonating gas is obtained in each jar as when a single jar is connected, though over a longer period of time. If the total amount of detonating gas is burnt, the energy obtained will evidently be much greater than the energy expended in charging the battery. In other words, the law of conservation of energy is broken. Explain the fallacy.

433. Find the e.m.f. E of a Daniel cell, given that 124,000 cal of heat are liberated when one gram-equivalent of zinc combines with sulphuric acid, and that approximately 99,700 cal are required to produce a gram-equivalent of copper from $CuSO_4$.

434. The ion mobilities in an electrolyte are u for the cations and v for the anions. Find the charge of ions of both types that pass through the electrolyte if a total of N coulombs of electricity is passed.

435. An electrolytic bath containing a $CuSO_4$ solution is connected in series with a silver voltmeter, in which 1 g silver is deposited on passage of the current. During the same time, the $CuSO_4$ solution surrounding the cathode loses 0·21 g copper as a result of electrolysis. What is the speed of the SO_4 anion relative to the Cu cation?

436. On electrolysis of a sulphuric acid solution the H cation moves 5·4 times faster than the SO_4 anion. Find the migration number.

437. An electrolytic bath contains a four per cent solution of silver nitrate ($AgNO_3$) at 18·4°C. When current passes through the electrolyte 0·3208 g silver is deposited at the cathode, whilst measurement of the silver concentration in the solution after electrolysis shows that only 0·1691 g silver disappears from near the cathode. What is the migration number k of silver?

438. A current of 0·43 amp is passed for 10 min through an electrolytic bath containing a weak solution of potassium chloride (KCl), after which a measurement of the concentration shows that 0·09964 g KCl has disappeared from the solution near the anode. Find the migration number k of potassium. The molecular weight of KCl is 74·6.

439. The following migration numbers were obtained for a concentrated solution of CdI_2 in water: for the anion $n = 1·258$, and for the cation $1 - n = -0·258$, i.e. more cadmium disappears from the cathodic part of the electrolyte than is deposited at the cathode. How can this be explained?

440. The concentrations of the electrolyte near two electrodes are c_1 and c_2. What is the work A done in compression of the cations due to their transfer from the anode to the cathode at constant temperature T of the electrolyte, if the mobilities of the anion and cation are u, v, and N units of electricity pass through the electrolyte.

441. The potential difference on the poles of a concentration cell is given by the Helmholtz formula

$$V_1 - V_2 = \frac{v - u}{v + u} \frac{RT}{nF} \ln \frac{c_1}{c_2}$$

(R is the gas constant, v, u are the ionic mobilities, n is the valency, F is Faraday's number). Obtain this formula by starting from the law of conservation of energy.

442. Find the relationship between the diffusion coefficient k and the mobility u of the corresponding ion.

443. The density of the electrolyte is known to increase during the charging of an acid accumulator. (Charging is usually stopped when the density reaches $1 \cdot 3$ gcm^{-3} instead of the initial $1 \cdot 1$ gcm^{-3}.) What is the reason for this increase in density during charging?

§ 8. THERMOELECTRICITY

444. A bismuth – iron thermocouple with constant $C = 92 \times 10^{-6}$ $V deg^{-1}$ and resistance $r = 5$ ohm is connected to a galvanometer with internal resistance $R = 110$ ohm. What is the galvanometer reading if one junction of the thermocouple is submerged in the steam of water boiling at normal temperature and the other in melting ice?

445. What is the constant C of a bismuth – tellurium thermocouple if, when it is connected to a galvanometer with internal resistance $R = 100$ ohm and sensitivity 10^{-8} amp per division, the minimum temperature difference which can be measured is $\Delta T = 2 \times 10^{-3} °C$? Neglect the resistance of the thermocouple.

446. The temperature of a furnace is measured by a nickel–nichrome thermocouple with constant $C = 0 \cdot 5 \times 10^{-6}$ $V deg^{-1}$, connected to a galvanometer with internal resistance $R = 2000$ ohm and sensitivity 10^{-8} amp per division. When the temperature of the second junction is $T_2 = +15 °C$ the galvanometer reading is $b = 25$ divisions. What is the temperature T of the furnace?

447. (1) Two different metals are in contact. The electronic gas pressure in the first metal is p_1 and the work function of an electron from the metal is A_1; the electronic gas pressure in the second metal is p_2 and the work function of an electron from it is A_2. Find the contact potential if the temperature of both metals is T. (2) A thermocouple is made from the above metals, the temperatures of its two junctions being T_1 and T_2. Find the thermoelectromotive force.

Hint. The electron gas pressure p in a metal is connected with the electron concentration n and the temperature T of the metal by $p = nkT$, where k is Boltzmann's constant.

§ 9. ELECTRONICS

448. What is the velocity v of an electron passing through a potential difference $V = 100$ V?

449. Find the mean velocity v of the ordered motion of electrons along a copper conductor, through which a constant current of density 1 ampcm^{-2} is flowing, assuming that there is one conductivity electron per copper atom in the metal.

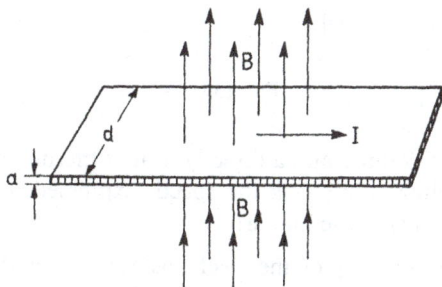

FIG. 138

450. A thin metal ribbon of width d (Fig. 138) is situated in a uniform magnetic field whose induction is B; the plane of the ribbon (thickness a) is perpendicular to B. A current I flows through the ribbon. Find the potential difference V obtained between the edges of the ribbon (i.e. at a distance d), if the concentration of the free electrons in the metal of the ribbon is n (a particular case of the Hall effect).

451. The following procedure can be used for finding the work function of an electron from a metal. A filament of the metal under test is stretched along the axis of a cylinder and the entire device placed *in vacuo*. When a current I_h is passed along the filament, it heats up to a temperature T and acquires a resistance R. A high positive potential is then applied to the cylinder, so as to obtain the saturation current I. The temperature of the filament now falls. In order to re-establish the previous temperature, the heating current is increased by ΔI_h. Calculate the work function φ in volts, assuming that I_h, T, R, ΔI_h are known. The influence of the cylinder temperature on the temperature T of the heated filament can be neglected.

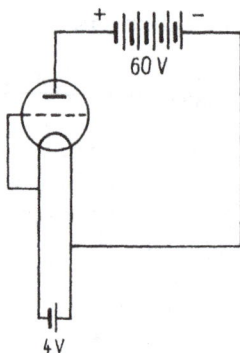

FIG. 139

452. Figure 139 illustrates a directly heated thermionic valve and the applied voltages. What is the speed (expressed in volts) with which electrons reach the anode?

453. Will the velocity of the electrons arriving at the anode be different if the grid is connected to the anode, and not to the heater as shown in Fig. 139?

454. An electron, leaving the heated cathode K with fairly low velocity, acquires a velocity in the field of an anode A subject to the potential V, and after passing through the plates of a condenser of length l, hits a fluorescent screen B (Fig. 140), situated at a distance D from the condenser. When an electric field is present in the condenser the spot on the screen is displaced a distance d. What is the field-strength E in the condenser?

455. Show that, whatever the velocity v_0 of an electron moving in a uniform magnetic field of intensity H, and whatever the angle α

($\neq 0$) formed by the direction of v_0 with the direction of H, it will describe one turn of a helix in the same time T.

456. An electron moving with velocity v arrives in a uniform magnetic field whose intensity H is perpendicular to v. What is the radius of the circle described by the electron?

457. An electron moves in a uniform magnetic field of intensity H. What is the work done by the force acting on the electron?

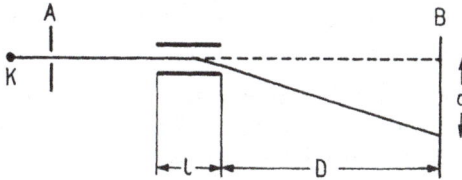

FIG. 140

458. An electron moves in a uniform magnetic field of intensity H (Fig. 141) and at the instant when it is at the point A it has a velocity v, forming an angle α with the direction of the field. After describing one turn of a helix, it arrives at the point B. What is the length of AB?

459· The diameter of the filament of a magnetron is d, and the diameter of the anode D. A potential difference V is applied between the filament and the anode. A wire is wound round the magnetron shell so as to form a solenoid whose axis coincides with the filament. The number of turns per unit length of the solenoid is n.

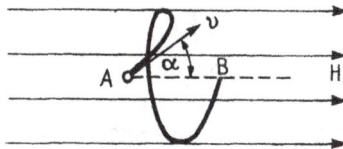

FIG. 141

What is the least current that must flow in the solenoid in order for an electron leaving the filament with zero initial velocity to be unable to reach the anode?

460. A uniform electric field of intensity E and a uniform magnetic field of intensity H are produced between two parallel plates, one of which is the cathode and the other the anode; the electric field is perpendicular to the plane of the plates and the magnetic field parallel to the plates. (1) Determine the motion of an electron that leaves the cathode surface with zero initial velocity. (2) In what conditions will the electron return to the cathode, and what will be its point of arrival?

461. What must be the direction and magnitude of the initial velocity of the electron in the previous problem if it is to describe a circle? What is the radius R of this circle? What is the period T of rotation of the electron round the circle?

462. An electron travels with velocity v in a uniform magnetic field of intensity H, perpendicular to v. Find the magnetic moment M of the equivalent current.

463. An electron travels with velocity v in a uniform magnetic field perpendicular to v. Find the angular momentum $\mathfrak{M}$ of the electron.

464. If it is assumed that the mass of a slowly moving electron, considered as a sphere of radius R with charge e, is of electromagnetic origin, it will be equal to $2e^2/3Rc^2$. It is found experimentally that $e/m = 1.77 \times 10^7$ e.m.u. for an electron. Find the radius R of an electron.

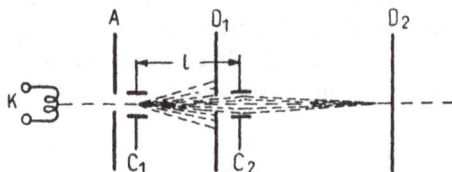

Fig. 142

465. An electron travelling with velocity v is incident in mutually perpendicular uniform electric and magnetic fields, the intensities of which are E and H respectively. The velocity v is perpendicular to both fields. Find how the electron moves.

466. What is the condition for the motion of the electron in the previous problem to be rectilinear and uniform?

467. In a vacuum tube, the electrons emitted by the cathode K (Fig. 142) are accelerated by the electric field of the anode A, which carries a potential V relative to the cathode. After passing through a slit in the anode, the electrons travel through a condenser C_1, through a slit in a diaphragm D_1, through a second condenser C_2, then arrive at a screen D_2. The same alternating voltage of angular frequency ω is applied to the condensers C_1 and C_2. This frequency is chosen so that the spot produced on the screen by the electron beam is not smeared out. Find e/m for an electron, if the distance between the condensers C_1 and C_2 is l.

468. In the model of a hydrogen atom, an electron of charge $-e$ moves uniformly in a circular orbit of radius a about the nucleus with the charge $+e$. If such an atom is placed in a weak electric field of intensity E normal to the plane of the orbit, the orbit of the

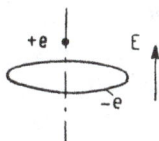

FIG. 143

electron is displaced (Fig. 143), and the atom acquires an electric dipole moment. Find the magnitude ϱ of this moment, neglecting the change in the distance between the charges.

469. Find the frequency of the electric field oscillations in a cyclotron, designed for acceleration of deuterons, if the magnetic field induction in the gap of the cyclotron magnets is 14,000 oersted.

470. Find the law of the magnification of the radius of the circles described by the deuterons in a cyclotron, knowing that the deuterons pass the gap between the dees when the voltage on them is a maximum.

471. The saturation current is $I_{sat} = 10^{-6}$ amp in a gas-discharge tube, with plane electrodes, cross-section $S = 10$ cm^2, spacing $d = 10$ cm. The ionisation in the tube occurs by external means. What is the number q of elementary charges of either sign produced per sec and per cm^3.

472. A potential difference V is applied to two plates, each of area S and spaced a distance d apart, forming a condenser *in vacuo*. On illuminating the cathode by ultraviolet rays, a current i passes between the plates, which reaches its saturation value I_{sat} when $V = V_0$. Find the electron mobility u.

473. A condenser C, whose plates A, B are spaced d apart, is mounted in a glass vessel containing gas. A small sheet of platinum, which is heated by current and leads to the formation of gas ions, is mounted at the centre of the plate A (Fig. 144). The centre of the plate B is cut out and a small aluminium plate fitted, one edge of the aluminium plate being attached to a thin stretched vertical wire. A potential difference is applied to the condenser plates and causes a current I to flow between them. Due to the presence of resistance in the medium the gas ions move uniformly. The aluminium plate attached to the wire is deflected through a small angle θ. The coefficient of torsional elasticity of the wire is c, the width of the small plate is l. Find the ion mobility u.

474. Two plane parallel electrodes are mounted in a gas-filled tube and a constant potential difference applied between them. The cathode is illuminated by a powerful light source, as a result of which n_0 electrons per sec leave the cathode surface. When the

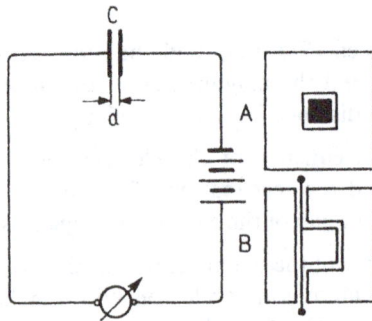

Fig. 144

electrons move in the electric field they ionise the gas molecules, and each electron produces α new electrons and ions per cm of its path. Neglecting ionisation of the gas molecules by the ions that are formed, calculate the electronic current I. The spacing between the electrodes is d.

475. The gas between two plane parallel electrodes, spacing d, is ionised by X-rays, n_0 electrons being produced per unit volume per sec. The electrons ionise the gas molecules as they move in the electric field between the electrodes, the ionisation coefficient being α. What is the current density I? Neglect the ionisation by positive ions.

476. The ionisation potential of a mercury atom is $\varphi = 10\cdot4$ V. What is the minimum velocity v required by an electron for it to ionise a mercury atom on collision?

477. A glow discharge is observed between the plane electrodes of a gas-discharge tube. What change occurs in the discharge if the anode is brought closer to the cathode?

478. What determines the shape of the equipotential surfaces in the positive column of a gas-discharge tube (Fig. 145)?

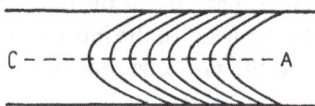

Fig. 145

479. Why do cathode rays form a straight beam, regardless of whether the anode lies in the path of the beam or is displaced to one side?

480. Two ions revolve about their common centre of mass; one carries a single positive charge, the other a single negative charge. The ion dimensions are very small compared with the distance between them. The ion pair is in thermal equilibrium with a monatomic gas whose temperature is $T = 3000\,^\circ\text{K}$. What is the electric moment of the pair?

§ 10. ELECTROMAGNETIC WAVES

481. Find the current amplitude I_x and voltage amplitude U_x distributions along the line for the natural oscillations in a twin line of length l, the ends of which are open circuit. Find the frequencies v of these oscillations. Losses in the line can be neglected.

482. Find the current amplitude I_x and voltage amplitude U_x distributions along the line for the natural oscillations in a twin line of length l, the ends of which are short-circuited. Find the frequencies v of these oscillations. Losses in the line can be neglected.

483. Find the current amplitude I_x and voltage amplitude U_x distributions along the line for the natural oscillations in a twin line of length l, one end of which is open circuit and the other end short-circuited. Find the frequencies ν of these oscillations. The losses in the line can be neglected.

484. Find the characteristic impedance ϱ of a lossless twin line, made of conductors of diameter $2r = 4$ mm, a distance $d = 10$ cm apart.

Hint. The characteristic impedance of a line is the ratio of the amplitude of the voltage of the wave travelling along the line to the amplitude of the current in the wave.

485. Find the characteristic impedance ϱ of a lossless air-spaced concentric line, the inner diameter of the outer cylinder of which is $2R = 40$ mm, and the diameter of the inner conductor $2r = 8$ mm.

Hint. See the hint to the previous problem.

486. Find the velocity v of electromagnetic wave propagation in a concentric line filled with dielectric of dielectric constant $\varepsilon = 4.5$. The losses in the cable can be neglected.

487. Find the periods T_n of the natural oscillations in a twin line of length l_1, open circuit at both ends and submerged in water. The losses in the line can be neglected.

488. Find the least frequency ν_1 at which resonance occurs in a concentric line, length $l = 12$ km, as described in Problem 486, if an a.c. source of negligible internal impedance is connected to one end and the other end is open circuit.

489. Find the characteristic impedance ϱ of a concentric line, the inner diameter of the outer conductor of which is $2R = 12$ mm, and the diameter of the inner conductor $2r = 2$ mm. The space between the conductors is filled with dielectric of dielectric constant $\varepsilon = 2.4$. The losses in the line can be neglected.

490. Find the input impedance of a lossless twin feeder at a frequency $\nu = 5 \times 10^7$ c/s if the feeder wires are of diameter $2R = 2$ mm, spaced $d = 12$ mm apart, and the end of the feeder is open circuit, the line length being (1) $l_1 = 2$ m; (2) $l_2 = 3$ m; (3) $l_3 = 3.5$ m; (4) $l_4 = 7.5$ m.

Determine whether the input impedance is capacitative or inductive.

Hint. The input impedance of a line at a given frequency is the ratio of the voltage to the current amplitude established at the input to the line when fed by an a.c. voltage of the frequency in question.

491. The wires of the feeder of the previous problem can be short-circuited by a metal bridge piece that can slide along the wires. Find the input impedance Z_{in} as a function of the distance x from the input to the bridge piece. Find how the nature of the impedance varies with the position of the bridge piece.

492. A section of lossless twin feeder 5 m long is terminated by a capacity of 20 pF. The distance between the feeder wires is $d = 4$ cm and the wire diameter is $2r = 4$ mm. Find the input impedance of the feeder at the frequency $v = 75 \times 10^6$ c/s.

Hint. When the line is terminated by a reactive (capacitative or inductive) load, the load can be replaced for purposes of calculation by a section of open-circuit line with the same characteristics as the original line, and with a length such that the input impedance of the section is equal to the reactive impedance of the load and is of the same kind (i.e. capacitative or inductive); thus the problem reduces to considering an equivalent unterminated line of a different length.

493. A section of concentric line 20 m long (the inner diameter of the outer line is 8 mm and the diameter of the inner line is 2 mm) filled with dielectric of dielectric constant $\varepsilon = 3\cdot2$, is terminated by a coil of inductance $L = 10$ μH. Find the input impedance of the section at the frequency $v = 15 \times 10^6$ c/s.

Hint. See the hint to the previous problem.

494. A twin line of length $l = 5$ m is made from wires diameter $2r = 3$ mm spaced $d = 6$ cm apart. Find the input impedance of the line for the frequency $v = 75 \times 10^6$ c/s, if the two wires together have a resistance $R = 0\cdot2$ ohm per metre, and the far end is (1) short-circuited, (2) open circuit.

Hint. In cases where the line length is an integral number of quarter waves, the line behaves like a series or parallel resonant circuit (depending on whether a current loop or node lies at the input end). This analogy can be used for finding the input impedance of a line, though it must be remembered that the current is different at different points of the line. Since the resistance of the line is small, the current distribution along it can be regarded as sinusoidal.

495. A twin line of length $l = 18$ m is terminated by a resistance $r = 80$ ohm. The characteristic impedance of the line is $\varrho = 400$ ohm. Losses in the line can be neglected. Find the input impedance of the line for wavelengths (1) $\lambda = 8$ m, (2) $\lambda = 9$ m.

Hint. Use the hint on the previous problem, to the effect that, when the line length is an integral number of quarter waves, it behaves like a series or parallel resonant circuit.

496. Find the input impedance of the line described in the previous problem, if it is terminated by a resistance $r = 400$ ohm.

497. Use the Poynting theorem to calculate the electromagnetic energy carried by a travelling wave propagated along a lossless air-spaced concentric cable. Show that the energy passing per unit time through a section of the cable is equal to the power supplied by the source which feeds the cable.

Hint. The electric and magnetic fields between the inner and outer conductors can be expressed in terms of the voltage and current in the line.

498. Find the distribution of the current amplitude I_x, the frequency ν and the wavelength λ of the natural oscillations in a thin wire of length $l = 6$ m when (1) it is mounted remote from the earth, (2) it is mounted vertically above the earth, the lower end being earthed.

Hint. It can be assumed for a thin wire that the natural oscillations yield the same current distribution as in a twin line under the same conditions.

499. In order to obtain very short electromagnetic waves, P. N. Lebedev, professor of physics at Moscow University, used a vibrator (Fig. 146), consisting of two thin platinum wires I and II, each 1·3 mm long, fused into glass tubes T_1 and T_2, and separated by a small (0·4 mm) spark gap. The device was charged from an induction coil via the wide spark-gaps between the connecting leads and the platinum wires. Prof. Lebedev produced by this means what were the shortest electromagnetic waves at that time (1895). What wavelength λ did the device give?

500. The electric and magnetic field-strengths in the wave produced by a sinusoidal current element (Hertz oscillator) whose dimensions are small compared with the wavelength, are given, at distances from the oscillator greater than the wavelength, by

$$E = 30(\omega l I/cr) \sin \varphi \sin \omega \left(t - \frac{r}{c} \right),$$

$$H = (1/4\pi) (\omega l I/cr) \sin \varphi \sin \omega \left(t - \frac{r}{c} \right),$$

where E is the electric field-strength in V/m, H is the magnetic field-strength in amp/m, ω is the angular frequency of the current in the oscillator, I is the current amplitude in amperes, l is the length of the oscillator, r is the distance from the oscillator to the point in question in metres, φ is the angle between the oscillator axis and the radius vector to the point. The directions of $\boldsymbol{E}$ and $\boldsymbol{H}$ are perpendicular to one another at every point, and perpendicular to the radius vector $\boldsymbol{r}$. Find the total power P radiated by the Hertz oscillator.

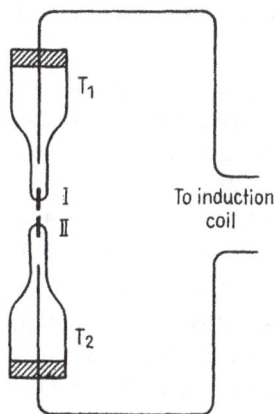

FIG. 146

Hint. It is necessary to find the mean value of the Poynting vector over the period of oscillation and integrate this value over a spherical surface, the centre of which is at the oscillator (the radius of the sphere may be arbitrary but must exceed the wavelength in order for the expressions given above for E and H to be valid).

501. Find the radiation resistance R_{rad} of a symmetric half-wave dipole.

Hint. The radiation resistance of a dipole is the ratio of the total power radiated to the square of the r.m.s. value of the current in the dipole loop. To calculate the total radiated power, we have to use the same method as in the previous problem, though remembering that the current is different in different sections of the dipole. Thus we have to split the dipole into individual elementary dipoles and calculate the field-strengths E and H due to each element then sum over the whole dipole. It can be assumed approximately that the fields due to the elements have the same phase at a given point of space.

502. Given the same simplifying assumptions as in the previous problem, find the radiation resistance R_{rad} of a quarter-wave aerial earthed at one end.

503. Currents of the same amplitude and phase are excited in two identical parallel dipoles spaced at a distance which is small compared with the wavelength. What is the radiation resistance R'_{rad} of each dipole? (The radiation resistance of a single half-wave dipole is $R = 72$ ohm.)

504. The radiation resistance of a full wave dipole (i.e. the length of the dipole accommodates one wave) is about 200 ohm. Explain why this radiation resistance is greater than the sum of the radiation resistances of two separate half-wave dipoles, and less than the sum of the radiation resistances of the two half-wave dipoles mounted in line as described in the previous problem.

505. Find the effective field-strength E_e produced by a half-wave dipole at a point on the equatorial plane of the dipole at a distance $r = 10$ km from it, given that the total radiated power $P = 10$ W.
Hint. Use the hints and the results of Problems 500 and 501.

506. Find the power incident on a parabolic reflector of diameter $D = 2$ m, if the reflector is directed towards a half-wave dipole, the radiation power of which is $P = 1$ kW, and lies on the equatorial plane of the dipole at a distance $r = 2$ km from it.
Hint. Use the hints and results of Problems 500 and 501.

507. What is the maximum power P_{max} that can be delivered to a receiver by a half-wave dipole of length $l = 3$ m connected to it, if the dipole is mounted parallel to the direction of the electric vector of the incident electromagnetic wave and the effective value of the electric field-strength of the wave is $E_e = 2\ \mu V/m$.

Hint. It is necessary to find the power developed by the electric field in the incident wave in each element of the dipole, in order to calculate the power developed in the whole dipole, then to find the part of this power which, given optimal matching conditions, can be transferred to the receiver.

508. Draw the polar diagram of a Hertz oscillator (see Problem 500) in the plane through the axis of the oscillator and in the plane perpendicular to this axis.

Hint. The polar diagram (for field-strength or power) is a curve such that its radius vector in a given direction has a length equal, on some given scale, to the field-strength (or energy flux density) produced by the dipole in this direction at a fixed distance.

509. Indicate qualitatively how the polar diagram of a dipole varies as its length increases from that of a Hertz oscillator to a half-wave.

510. Determine qualitatively the shape of the polar diagrams in the equatorial plane of aerials consisting of two half-wave dipoles mounted parallel to one another a half wavelength apart, and fed by currents of the same amplitude and frequency and (1) the same phase, (2) opposite phase.

511. Determine qualitatively the shape of the polar diagram in the equatorial plane of an aerial consisting of two half-wave dipoles, mounted parallel to one another a wavelength apart and fed by currents of the same amplitude and frequency and in opposite phase.

512. Determine qualitatively the shape of the polar diagram in the equatorial plane of an aerial consisting of two half-wave dipoles, mounted parallel to one another a quarter wavelength apart and fed by currents of the same amplitude and frequency and with a phase difference of $\frac{1}{2}\pi$.

513. Determine qualitatively the shape of the polar diagram in the equatorial plane of an aerial consisting of eight parallel half-wave dipoles, mounted a half wavelength apart along a straight line and fed by currents of the same amplitude, frequency and phase. Find the angular width of the main lobe of the diagram (i.e. the lobe in which the field-strength has its maximum) and estimate the ratio of the field-strength in the main lobe to the maximum in the first side-lobe.

514. Determine qualitatively the shape of the polar diagram of a half-wave dipole mounted horizontally above the earth in the equatorial (i.e. vertical) plane, if the earth can be regarded as ideally conducting and the height h of the dipole above the earth is equal to (1) a quarter wavelength, (2) half a wavelength. Find the directions in the equatorial plane of the maxima φ_{max} and minima (zeros) φ_{min} of the radiation of the dipole in the general case, when its height above the earth is $h = n\lambda$, where λ is the wavelength.

Hint. Since the earth is ideally conducting, a mirror image method can be used as in problems of electrostatics.

515. Determine qualitatively the shape of the polar diagram in the vertical plane of a vertical quarter-wave dipole, the lower end of which is earthed. Regard the earth as ideally conducting.

516. Find the directions of the maxima and minima in the vertical plane of the radiation from a vertical half-wave dipole when the height of the dipole above the earth (measuring from the dipole centre) is $h = n\lambda$, where λ is the wavelength.

Hint. See the hint to Problem 514.

517. A plane square frame aerial has a side $d = 50$ cm and $n = 10$ turns of wire. An a.c. current of r.m.s. value $I_e = 5$ amp and angular frequency $\omega = 5 \times 10^6$ c/s flows through the winding. Find the effective field-strength E_e of the electric field produced by this current in a direction perpendicular to the side of the frame and lying in the plane of the frame at a distance $r = 1$ km from it, and compare it with the field-strength in the equatorial plane of a Hertz oscillator having a length equal to the side of the frame and fed by the same current.

Hint. Since the length of the frame wire is small compared with the wavelength, it can be assumed that the current is the same in all sections of the frame, and the expression for the field of a Hertz oscillator (see Problem 500) can be used for calculating the field-strength.

518. Draw the polar diagram for a plane rectangular frame aerial whose dimensions are small compared with the wavelength in the plane perpendicular to the plane of the frame.

519. The plane square frame aerial, whose dimensions are given in Problem 517, is situated in the field of an electromagnetic wave, the plane of the frame being in the direction of the wave propagation, and the electric field of the wave parallel to one of the sides of the frame. The electric field-strength of the incident wave is $E = 50 \; \mu V/m$ and the angular frequency $\omega = 5 \times 10^6$ c/s. Find the e.m.f. produced by the wave in the frame, and compare it with the e.m.f. which the wave produces in a piece of wire whose length is equal to a side of the frame.

520. Find the speed v of propagation of a harmonic electromagnetic wave in a uniform layer of the ionosphere, if the angular frequency of the wave is $\omega = 8 \times 10^7$ c/s and the concentration of free electrons in the layer is $N = 1 \times 10^6$ cm^{-3}.

Hint. The influence of the free electrons on the speed of the wave propagation can be determined by considering the electron displacement due to the action of the electric field of the incident wave as a "polarisation" of the ionosphere, as a result of which the electric induction in the ionosphere is different from the electric field-strength. The ratio of these magnitudes is the dielectric constant of the ionosphere for high frequency fields.

521. The refraction of radio waves in the ionosphere (as a result of which they return to earth) can be regarded, in a simplified picture, as the total internal reflection from a sharp boundary of the ionosphere. Use this picture to find the shortest wavelength λ_{min} which returns to earth if its angle of incidence on the boundary of the ionosphere (the angle with the normal to the boundary) is $\varphi = 45°$, and the electron concentration in the ionosphere is $N = 1 \times 10^6$ cm^{-3}.

Hint. Use the results of the previous problem.

ANSWERS AND SOLUTIONS

§ 1. ELECTROSTATICS

1. $F \approx 918$ kg.

2. $F \approx 23 \times 10^{-4}$ dyne.

3. $q = 2786$ e.s.u.

4. The equilibrium will be unstable.

Solution. We take the case when the central charge is of opposite sign to the two other charges. If this charge is moved slightly along the line joining the three charges, the attraction due to the nearer charge increases, whilst that due to the more remote charge diminishes, with the result that the charge moves still further from the equilibrium position. Its equilibrium is therefore unstable.

If the central charge is of the same sign as the other two, and it moves slightly along the line joining the charges, forces will arise that tend to return it to its equilibrium position. However, if it moves at right angles to the line joining the charges, the resultant of the repulsions will no longer be zero and will act in the direction in which it has moved. As a result the charge will tend to move further from its equilibrium position. The equilibrium is thus unstable.

This result, which we have obtained for an elementary case, is always valid. If only Coulomb forces of interaction are present in a system of free electric charges, the equilibrium is always unstable.

5. $e_1 = \dfrac{2\sqrt{2} + 1}{4}\, e$ (the equilibrium is unstable).

6. $e_1 = \dfrac{e}{\sqrt{3}}$ (the equilibrium is unstable).

7. Since the sum of the charges in the system as a whole is not zero, and the conductor A does not enclose the charges e, part of the lines of forces from e must go to infinity (or terminate on other conductors), and only a fraction of the lines of force from e terminate in the induced charge. The induced charge is thus less than e.

8. The field is perpendicular to the surface of the layer and is directed as shown in Fig. 147(a). Outside the layer $E = \pm 2\pi\varrho d$, inside the layer $E = 4\pi\varrho x$. The x axis is perpendicular to the surface, and $x = 0$ at the centre of the layer. The variation of the field-strength E as a function of x is illustrated in Fig. 147(b).

9. $e = \dfrac{mg \tan \varphi}{2\pi\sigma} = 9$ e.s.u.

10. $E = \dfrac{8\sigma d}{d^2 + 4x^2}$.

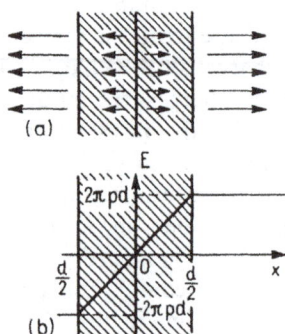

FIG. 147

11. $E = 2\pi\sigma\left(1 - \dfrac{h}{\sqrt{h^2 + R^2}}\right) = \sigma\Omega$,

where Ω is the solid angle subtended by the disc at the given point.

12. The plane of symmetry between the two point charges $+e$ and $-e$ is the plane of zero potential. The field pattern is therefore unchanged if an infinite conducting sheet is placed in this plane. The field produced by the charge $+e$ and the charges induced on the conducting plane will thus be identical to the field of the two point charges $+e$ and $-e$ (considered, of course, from one side of the plane of symmetry). The forces acting on the charge $+e$ must therefore be the same in both cases.

13. $E = \dfrac{e}{5h^2} \sqrt{26 - 2\sqrt{5}}$.

Hint. The field produced by the charges induced on the conducting surface can be regarded as the field of the point charge $-e$ situated at a distance h behind the plane, symmetric to the basic charge $+e$ (see the solution of the previous problem).

14. $V = 2\pi\sigma d$.

15. See Fig. 148. The sketch shows the distribution of the lines of force in the plane through the given charges. The continuous lines are the lines of force, the dotted lines are the equipotential lines. The line through the point A divides the lines of force of the charge $+e$ from the lines of force of the charge $+4e$. The point A is at a distance $2d/3$ from the charge $4e$. The field potential at the points B and D is equal to the potential at A:

$$\varphi_A = \frac{4e}{\frac{2}{3}d} + \frac{e}{\frac{1}{3}d} = \frac{9e}{d}.$$

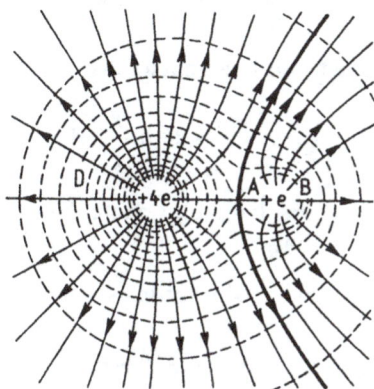

Fig. 148

The distance from the charge $4e$ to the point D is d_1 and can be found from the equations $\varphi_D = (4e/d_1) + (e/(d + d_1)) = \varphi_A$, or $d_1 = d(2\sqrt{10} - 2)/9$. Similarly, the distance from the charge e to the point B is found to be $d_2 = d(\sqrt{13} - 2)/9$. At a very great distance from the charges the equipotential lines must be almost circles.

16. $R = \dfrac{dn}{n^2 - 1}; \quad x_0 = -\dfrac{d}{n^2 - 1}.$

Hint. Take as the origin the point at which the smaller charge is situated, direct the x axis towards the greater charge and write down the potential at the point (x, y) of the plane through the line joining the charges, then equate this to zero.

17. We consider the field in the plane perpendicular to the conductors. At any point M of the plane the field potential is the sum of the potentials due to each conductor. If r is the distance of M from a conductor, the potential due to the left-hand conductor is

$$V_1 = \int \frac{2\sigma}{r}\, dr = 2\sigma \ln r_1 + C_1.$$

Similarly, the potential due to the right-hand conductor is

$$V_2 = -\int \frac{2\sigma}{r}\, dr = -2\sigma \ln r_2 + C_2.$$

The potential due to both conductors is

$$V = V_1 + V_2 = 2\sigma \ln \frac{r_1}{r_2} + C_1 + C_2. \tag{1}$$

Since, when M becomes infinitely remote, $V \to 0$ and $\ln (r_1/r_2) \to 0$, it follows from (1) that

$$V = 2\sigma \ln \frac{r_1}{r_2}.$$

If $r_1/r_2 = k$ is constant, V is also constant. We take the projection of the left-hand conductor on to the plane as the origin and the straight line through the projections of the two conductors as the x axis. The equipotential lines are now given by (Fig. 149):

$$\frac{r_1}{r_2} = k = \frac{1}{\sqrt{x^2 + y^2}} : \frac{1}{\sqrt{(d - x)^2 + y^2}},$$

whence

$$\left(x + \frac{d}{k^2 - 1}\right)^2 + y^2 = \frac{k^2 d^2}{(k^2 - 1)^2}.$$

This is the equation of a circle of radius $R = kd/|k^2 - 1|$ and centre the point O, the abscissa of which is $a = -d/(k^2 - 1)$. Since in the present case,

$$OA \cdot OB = (-a)(-a + d) = \frac{k^2 d^2}{(k^2 - 1)^2} = R^2 = OM^2,$$

OM can be regarded as the length of the segment of the tangent to the circle passing through the points A, M, B. Its centre lies on the straight line through the mid-point of AB and perpendicular to AB.

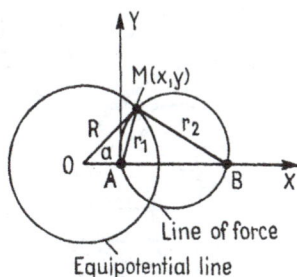

Fig. 149

The tangents to the two circles are therefore perpendicular at their point of intersection. A unique equipotential line can be drawn through any point M of the circle AMB, so that the circle AMB is a line of force.

18. See Fig. 150. The figure illustrates the field in an arbitrary plane through the charges. All the lines of force lying in the region bounded by the heavy line through the point A, at which the field-strength is zero, travel from the charge $+e$ to the charge $-4e$, whilst the remainder travel off to infinity. The distance from the point A to the charge $+e$ is d. The potential at the point B is zero, so that a spherical equipotential surface passes through B, the radius of which is $4d/15$, whilst its centre is at a distance $d/15$ from the charge $+e$ (see Problem 16).

19. $e' = \dfrac{e}{2}$.

Solution. The surface of the metal sphere has zero potential (since the sphere is earthed). We obtain the same surface of zero potential and the same field outside it if we remove the sphere and replace it with a charge $e' = \frac{1}{2}e$ at the point of the straight line joining the charge to the centre of the sphere at a distance $\frac{1}{2}R$ from the centre (see Problem 16).

20. The potential distribution is the same in all planes at right angles to the charged line. The equipotential surfaces are coaxial cylinders whose axis is the charged line. The potential difference between the cylinders of radii R_1 and R_2 $(R_2 > R_1)$ is equal to

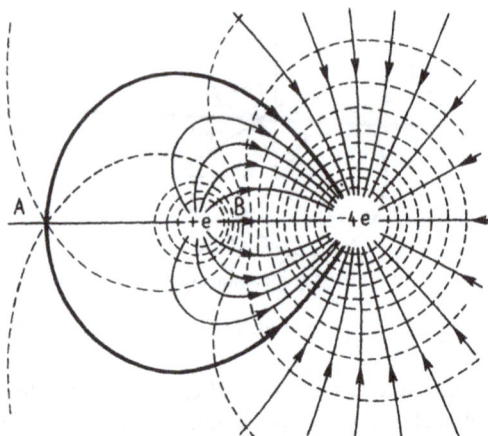

Fig. 150

$2\sigma \ln (R_2/R_1)$. But the potential does not have a finite value at infinity, since the work of the field forces when the $+1$ charge is removed from the given point (R_1) to infinity does not have a finite value. It is only the potential difference between two points of the field that has a finite value.

This result is due to the fact that we regard the conductor as infinite, i.e. we cannot speak of points infinitely remote from the conductor, since an "infinitely remote point" means physically a point which is at a distance large compared with the conductor dimensions.

Such difficulties do not arise when considering real fields, since the conductor dimensions are finite. Any charged conductor can be regarded as a point if the distance from it is sufficiently great. Thus, if we agree conventionally to regard a real conductor as infinite, we can only calculate the near-by field (at a distance small compared with the length of the conductor).

21. $V = 4\pi\sigma r \ln \dfrac{d}{r}$.

Hint. The field-strength at the point a distance $x > r$ from the cylinder axis is $4\pi r\sigma/x$.

22. The field is parallel to the x axis and its intensity is $E = ax$. Such a field will exist inside a layer bounded by infinite planes perpendicular to the x axis, charged uniformly with the spatial density $\varrho = a/4\pi$ (see Problem 8).

23. $e = 5.92 \times 10^5$ Coulombs, $\varphi = 2.7 \times 10^5$ e.s.u. $= 8.2 \times 10^8$ V.

24. (1) $E = \dfrac{2e}{h^2}$, (2) $E = \dfrac{8e}{9h^2}$.

Hint. See Problem 12.

25. $E = \dfrac{4}{5\sqrt{5}} \dfrac{e}{d^2}$; the field is perpendicular to the plane and directed towards it.

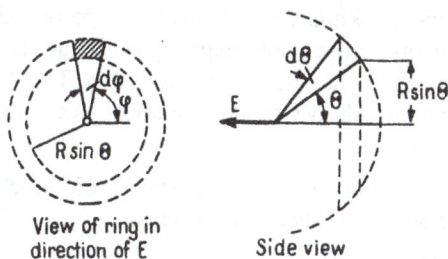

View of ring in direction of E

Side view

FIG. 151

26. (1) No. (2) There will be inside, but not outside.

27. $E = \pi\sigma$.

Solution. The field-strength produced at the centre of a sphere of radius R by the charges on a ring of width $Rd\theta$, cut from a hemisphere carrying the charge density σ will, by symmetry, be perpendicular to the plane of the ring (see Fig. 151). Thus we only take into account the normal component to the plane of the ring when calculating the field-strength due to the charge on each element of the ring. This component is obviously equal to

$$\frac{\sigma R^2 \sin \theta \cos \theta \, d\theta}{R^2} \, d\varphi.$$

On integrating from 0 to 2π with respect to φ, we obtain the field-strength due to the charges on the ring:

$$2\pi\sigma \sin \theta \cos \theta \, d\theta.$$

On integrating from 0 to $\frac{1}{2}\pi$ with respect to θ, we find that the field-strength produced by the charge on the first half of the sphere is

$$E = \pi\sigma.$$

The field produced by the charges on the second half of the sphere will be in the opposite direction, and of magnitude $2\pi\sigma$. Consequently, the resultant field-strength at the centre of the sphere is equal to $\pi\sigma$, and its direction is opposite to that of the field-strength E shown in Fig. 151.

28. There is no change outside the envelope, inside the field-strength is reduced in the ratio $1/\varepsilon$.

29. Generally speaking, the field will change outside as well as inside the envelope, the change being specially noticeable close to an "irregularity" in the dielectric boundary. The "irregularity" must be estimated relative to the spherical boundary of the dielectric.

30. It increases, since the surface density of the charge on the metal plate opposite the dielectric increases.

31. $Q = ER^2 = 22{,}500$ e.s.u.

32. $p = 2\pi\sigma^2 = \dfrac{2\pi Q^2}{(4\pi R^2)^2} = \dfrac{Q^2}{8\pi R^4}.$

Hint. Let σ be the charge density on the sphere. The field-strength outside the surface of the sphere is $4\pi\sigma$, and inside is zero. We separate fictitiously an element dS of the surface. The field at the surface can be regarded as the result of superimposing two fields: (1) the field due to the charges on the element dS and producing the field-strength $2\pi\sigma$ outside and inside, and (2) the field due to the rest of the charge; consequently, the field due to the rest of the charge is $2\pi\sigma$ and is directed outwards. Thus the force acting from within on the element dS is $2\pi\sigma^2 dS$. The pressure is therefore $2\pi\sigma^2$.

33. The forces acting per unit area of the uncharged soap bubble are: (1) the pressure force, inversely proportional to the volume of the bubble, i.e. proportional to $1/R^3$ and acting outwards; (2) the force of surface tension, proportional to $1/R$ and directed inwards. With a given radius R, these forces balance one another:

$$\frac{a}{R^3} - \frac{c}{R} = 0,$$

where the constants a and c depend on the concrete conditions of the experiment. On communicating a charge to the soap bubble, we add to the force acting outwards the force of electrostatic repulsion of the charges (see Problem 32), proportional to $1/R^4$. We must have, for equilibrium,

$$\frac{a}{R_1^3} + \frac{b}{R_1^4} - \frac{c}{R_1} = 0.$$

Hence, we can obtain the relationship between the variation of the forces acting per unit surface of the bubble and the variation ΔR_1 of the radius:

$$\Delta p = -\left(\frac{3a}{R_1^3} + \frac{4b}{R_1^4} - \frac{c}{R_1}\right)\frac{\Delta R_1}{R_1},$$

where the quantity in brackets is positive. The equilibrium is therefore stable. An increase in R_1 leads to a greater decrease in the forces acting outwards, so that the resultant force will diminish the radius, i.e. will return it to the equilibrium value R_1. Conversely, a decrease in the radius leads to a greater increase in the same forces, and the resultant force will increase the radius.

34. The field inside the sphere is zero, so that the potential φ has a constant value, equal to the potential on the sphere itself, i.e. $4\pi R\sigma$, whilst outside the sphere the potential is $4\pi R^2\sigma/d$ (the thin line in Fig. 152). Inside the sphere, E is zero, whilst outside $E = 4\pi R^2\sigma/d^2$ (the heavy line in Fig. 152).

35. The field will be as shown in Fig. 153.

The potential of the outer sphere is Q/R_3, and of the inner $Q(1/R_1 - 1/R_2 + 1/R_3)$. If the outer sphere is earthed, its potential will be zero, and the potential of the inner sphere will be

$$Q(R_2 - R_1)/R_1 R_2.$$

36. See Fig. 154 (a and b).

$$E_0 = 0 \cdot 1 \text{ e.s.u.,} \quad \varphi_0 = \frac{3}{2} \text{ e.s.u.} = 450 \text{ V.}$$

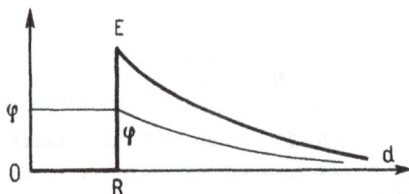

FIG. 152

37. Part of the lines of force starting from the charge $+2e$ will terminate on the inner side of the closed envelope, i.e. the potential of the latter will be lower than the potential of the conductor having the charge $+2e$.

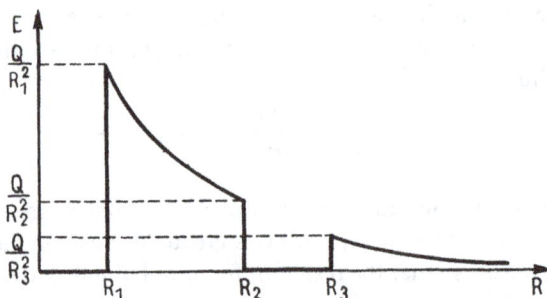

FIG. 153

38. A charge of opposite sign, equal to half the charge on the bubble. See Problem 32.

39. $E = 2\sqrt{5}\, \pi\sigma$ (Fig. 155).

40. The equipotential surfaces of the field are planes inclined at an angle φ, given by $\tan \varphi = 2$, to the charged plane with charge density σ. The potential varies linearly with the distance from the line of intersection of the surfaces. For the surface with charge density $2\sigma : V = -2\pi\sigma x + c$. For the surface with charge density $\sigma : V = -4\pi\sigma z + c$.

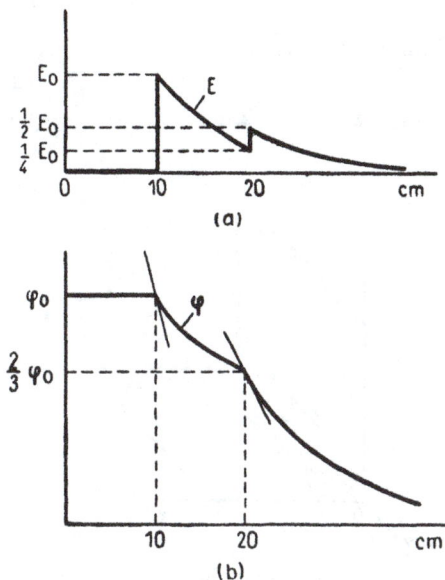

(a)

(b)

Fig. 154

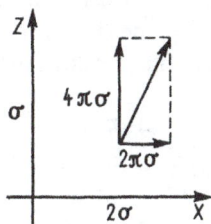

Fig. 155

41. $\sigma = 0.00265$ e.s.u.

42. $R = 1$ m.

43. Inside the cylinder the field is the same as in Problem 39. Outside the cylinder, if we take the cylinder axis as the Y axis, the first charged plane as the YOZ coordinate plane, and the second as the

XOY coordinate plane (Fig. 156), the field-strength components at an arbitrary point $A(X, Y, Z)$ will be:

along the X axis: $2\pi\sigma\left[1 - \dfrac{6Rx}{(x^2 + z^2)}\right]$,

along the Y axis: 0,

along the Z axis: $2\pi\sigma\left[2 - \dfrac{6Rz}{(x^2 + z^2)}\right]$.

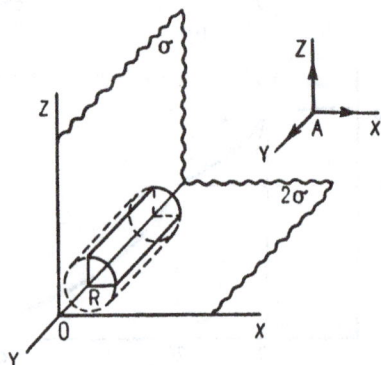

FIG. 156

44. If we locate the origin at the centre of the sphere and take the Z axis at right angles to the plane (Fig. 157), the field-strength at a point $A(X, Y, Z)$ outside the sphere will have the components along the coordinate axes:

X axis: $\dfrac{4\pi R^2\sigma x}{(x^2 + y^2 + z^2)^{3/2}}$,

Y axis: $\dfrac{4\pi R^2\sigma y}{(x^2 + y^2 + z^2)^{3/2}}$,

Z axis: $2\pi\sigma\left[1 + \dfrac{2R^2z}{(x^2 + y^2 + z^2)^{3/2}}\right]$.

At a point inside the sphere the field is directed along the Z axis and is equal to $2\pi\sigma$.

45. $\varrho = 1\cdot3 \times 10^{-3}$ e.s.u. m^{-3}.

46. (1) 40 V, (2) Zero between plates 1 and 2, and 40 V between plates 2 and 3.

47. 40 V.

48. The field-strength in the direction from point 1 to point 2 is $E_{12} = (V_1 - V_2)/a$, where a is the length of side of the cube. Similarly, $E_{13} = (V_1 - V_3)/a$ and $E_{14} = (V_1 - V_4)/a$. The vector sum of E_{12}, E_{13}, E_{14} gives the approximate magnitude of the field-strength at the point 1.

49. $V_{12} \approx 0\cdot25$ e.s.u.; $V_{23} \approx 0\cdot75$ e.s.u.

50. It is halved.

51. $V \approx 189$ V.

52. At a distance R cm from the common axis of the cylinders $E \approx 39/R$ e.s.u.

53. $A = \dfrac{\mu e}{R^2}$.

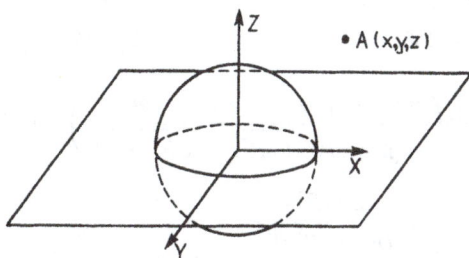

FIG. 157

54. No, since such a field would not be lamellar. For, the work done in moving a charge along a rectangular closed contour, two sides of which are parallel to the field, and two at right angles to it (Fig. 158), will be non-zero.

55. The conductor potential is reduced.

56. It is reduced.

57. $V = 2\pi \dfrac{ed}{S}$.

58. See Fig. 159. $E \approx 6\pi \dfrac{e}{S}$.

59. $V = \dfrac{Q(R_2 - R_1)}{R_1 R_2} = 750$ V.

The field-strength inside the first sphere is zero, between the spheres it is Q/R^2, outside the second sphere it is $2Q/R^2$, where R is the distance from the observation point to the centre of the spheres.

60. (1) $V = 9 \times 10^8$ V, (2) The charge is not retained, since the field-strength at the surface of the sphere will be $E = 90$ kV/mm.

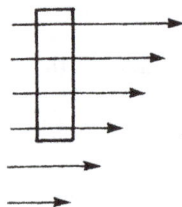

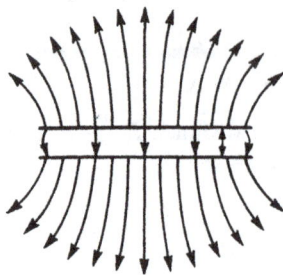

Fig. 158   Fig. 159

61. $E = 2\pi\sigma\left(\dfrac{h + d}{\sqrt{(h + d)^2 + R^2}} - \dfrac{h}{\sqrt{h^2 + R^2}}\right)$, see Problem 11.

If $d \ll h$, $E \approx \dfrac{2\pi\sigma R^2 d}{(h^2 + R^2)^{3/2}}$.

62. $Q \approx 265$ e.s.u.

63. It is increased one and a half times.

64. It is increased by 200 pF. The position of the foil has no effect on the result when it remains parallel to the coatings.

65. $C = 35$ cm.

66. $C = \dfrac{r}{2}$.

Hint. If $r \ll R$, where R is the distance between the spheres, the capacity of one sphere relative to the plane of symmetry is roughly equal to r. The capacity between the spheres can therefore be regarded as the capacity of two condensers connected in series.

67. $C = \dfrac{C_{ag}C_{af} + C_{ag}C_{gf} + C_{gf}C_{af}}{C_{gf} + C_{ag}}$.

68. $C_{af} = \dfrac{C_1 - C_2 + C_3}{2}$; $\quad C_{ag} = \dfrac{-C_1 + C_2 + C_3}{2}$;

$C_{gf} = \dfrac{C_1 + C_2 - C_3}{2}$.

69. (1) The capacity is greater in case a;
(2) $C_4 = C_1 C_2/(C_1 + C_2)$, C_3 can have any value.

70. For a cylindrical condenser

$$C = \frac{l}{2 \ln (R_2/R_1)}.$$

If $R_2 = R_1 + \Delta R$, then

$$\ln \frac{R_2}{R_1} = \ln \left(1 + \frac{\Delta R}{R_1}\right) \approx \frac{\Delta R}{R_1}.$$

Now

$$C = \frac{lR_1}{2\,\Delta R} = \frac{2\pi R_1 l}{4\pi\,\Delta R} = \frac{S}{4\pi\,\Delta R},$$

where S is the lateral surface of the cylinder. The proof is similar for a spherical condenser.

71. $lr = \text{const}$, where l is the length of the tube, r is its radius. The bushings are used to achieve a more uniform potential drop in the insulation, and hence a reduction in the maximum value of the field-strength on the insulation. If a single insulating tube has a thickness of the order of the conductor radius, the field-strength at the conductor is roughly twice that at the tube surface, whereas in the case of a condenser bushing with very thin layers the field-strength is more or less the same everywhere.

72. It is roughly doubled.

73. It is increased to roughly three times that of the capacity of the condenser without a cover.

74. $V_1 = \dfrac{VC_2}{C_1 + C_2}$ and $V_2 = \dfrac{VC_1}{C_1 + C_2}$, where V_1 is the voltage across the condenser C_1 and V_2 the voltage across C_2.

75. $V_1 = 3 \text{ V};$ $V_2 = 1 \cdot 5 \text{ V};$ $V_3 = 3 \text{ V};$ $V_4 = 1 \cdot 5 \text{ V}.$

76. $V_1 = 3 \cdot 6 \text{ V};$ $V_2 = 1 \cdot 8 \text{ V};$ $V_3 = 3 \cdot 6 \text{ V};$ $V_4 = 1 \cdot 8 \text{ V}.$

77. $V_1 = \dfrac{C_1 E_1 + C_2 E_2}{C_1 + C_2},$ $V_2 = \dfrac{C_1 (E_2 - E_1)}{C_1 + C_2}.$

Hint. The charges on the condenser coatings are connected by the equation $e_1 - e_2 = C_1 E_1$, as follows from the law of conservation of charge.

78. Its electrical capacity must be much less than the capacity of the conductor, in order for the conductor potential not to change on joining up the electroscope.

79. $V = 1413 \text{ V}.$

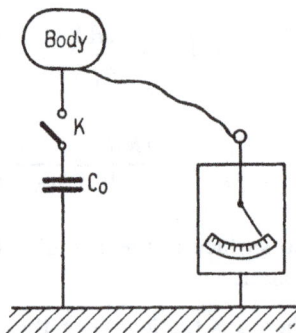

FIG. 160

80. (1) $E_1 = 6 \cdot 28$ e.s.u., (2) $E_2 = 3 \cdot 14$ e.s.u., (3) the repulsive force is $F = 12 \cdot 6$ dyne.

81. By using the values of V_1, V_2 and C_0, we can find the capacity of the charged body and electrometer relative to earth (Fig. 160). This capacity is given by $C_x = C_0 V_2 / (V_1 - V_2)$. The charge is equal to $e = C_x V_1$. The accuracy of determination of the charge depends on the magnitudes of V_1 and V_2, and in addition, on $V_1 - V_2$. The greater $V_1 - V_2$, the more accurate the determination of the charge.

82. $V = 17 \cdot 25 \text{ kV}$.

83. $C = \dfrac{\varepsilon_1 \varepsilon_2 S}{4\pi[d_1(\varepsilon_2 - \varepsilon_1) + d\varepsilon_1]}$.

84. (1) $C_1 = \dfrac{S}{2\pi d\left(\dfrac{1}{\varepsilon_1} + \dfrac{1}{\varepsilon_2}\right)}$; (2) $C_2 = \dfrac{S(\varepsilon_1 + \varepsilon_2)}{8\pi d}$; $C_2 > C_1$,

since $(\varepsilon_1 + \varepsilon_2)^2$ is always greater than $2\varepsilon_1\varepsilon_2$.

85. $C = \dfrac{S\varepsilon_1\varepsilon_2}{4\pi nd(\varepsilon_1 + \varepsilon_2)}$.

86. $C = \dfrac{S(\varepsilon_1 - \varepsilon_2)}{4\pi d \ln \dfrac{\varepsilon_1}{\varepsilon_2}}$.

Hint. Since the variation of the dielectric constant between the plates is given by $\varepsilon = \varepsilon_1 + x(\varepsilon_2 - \varepsilon_1)/d$ where x is the distance from the first plate, the potential difference between the coatings can be written as

$$V = \int_0^d E dx = Dd \int_0^d \frac{dx}{\varepsilon_1 d + (\varepsilon_2 - \varepsilon_1)x},$$

where E is the field-strength, $D = 4\pi\sigma$ is the electric induction.

87. It is increased by $V(\varepsilon - 1)/4\pi d$.

88. $E = \dfrac{\varepsilon V}{(D - d)\varepsilon + d} \approx 1750 \text{ V cm}^{-1}$.

89. $C = \dfrac{(\varepsilon + 1)Rr}{2(R - r)} = 120 \text{ cm}$.

90. At a point a distance R from the centre of the sphere $(5 < R < 7)$ the intensity is $E = 1000/R^2$ e.s.u.

91. $E' = \dfrac{(\varepsilon - 1)E}{3}$. If P is the polarisation vector of the di-

electric medium, we have $(\varepsilon - 1)E = 4\pi P$. The field-strength at
the centre of the spherical cavity is $E' = 4\pi P/3$. For (Fig. 161):

$$E' = \int_0^\pi d\Theta \int_0^{2\pi} \frac{P \cos \Theta \cdot R^2 \sin \Theta \, d\varphi}{R^2} \cos \Theta$$

$$= 2\pi P \int_0^\pi \sin \Theta \cos^2 \Theta \, d\Theta = \frac{4\pi}{3} P.$$

92. When the inner sphere is earthed, the system can be regarded
as a spherical condenser in parallel with the outer sphere, which has
a capacity R_2 relative to an infinitly remote sphere.

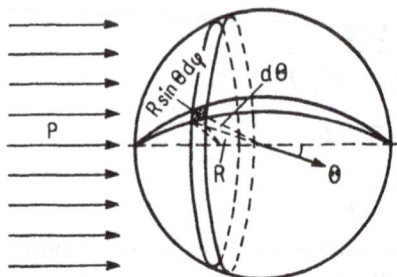

FIG. 161

93. $E = \dfrac{V}{d \ln 2}$.

94. There is no change.

95. $\varrho = -\dfrac{V_0}{2\pi d^2}$.

Solution. If x is the distance from the plate with potential V_0,
by Gauss's theorem the field-strength is given by $\partial E/\partial x = 4\pi\varrho$.
Since the potential V is connected with the field-strength by the
equation $E = - dV/dx$, we have $d^2V/dx^2 = - 4\pi\varrho$. The general
solution of the last equation is

$$V = - 2\pi\varrho x^2 + Cx + C_1.$$

The constants C, C_1 and hence the answer, are found by taking
into account the conditions of the problem.

96. At a point whose distance from the axis of the cylinders is r, the potential is

$$V = \frac{V_0 + \pi\varrho(R_2^2 - R_1^2)}{\ln \dfrac{R_2}{R_1}} \ln \frac{r}{R_1} - \pi\varrho(r^2 - R_1^2).$$

Solution. By Gauss's theorem, for an annular layer of radius r and thickness dr:

$$E\,2\pi r - \left(E - \frac{dE}{dr}\,dr\right) 2\pi(r - dr) = 4\pi\varrho\,2\pi r\,dr,$$

where E is the field-strength. Hence

$$\frac{dE}{dr} + \frac{1}{r}E = 4\pi\varrho,$$

or, for the potential,

$$\frac{d^2V}{dr^2} + \frac{1}{r}\frac{dV}{dr} = -4\pi\varrho.$$

A particular solution of this equation is

$$V_1 = -\pi\varrho r^2.$$

The solution of the corresponding homogeneous equation $d^2V/dr^2 + (1/r)dV/dr = 0$, has the form

$$V_2 = C\ln r + C_1.$$

The general solution of the non-homogeneous equation is therefore

$$V = V_1 + V_2 = C\ln r + C_1 - \pi\varrho r^2.$$

If we substitute in this the values of the potential given in the conditions of the problem, we find C and C_1, and obtain the answer.

97. Only extensions, normal to the plate.

98. $A = \dfrac{2\pi Q^2}{S}(d_0 - d)$. The energy of the electrostatic field of the condenser.

99. The required power varies inversely with the square of the distance:

$$W = \frac{SV^2}{8\pi x^2} \frac{dx}{dt},$$

where S is the area of the condenser plate, x is the distance between them, V is the potential difference and t is time.

Mechanical work is expended in moving the plates apart, and the electrostatic energy of the condenser is reduced, since it is equal to $\frac{1}{2}CV^2$, and C is reduced. But charge now flows from the condenser plates, i.e. it moves in opposition to the e.m.f. of the source. Both mechanical work and the released energy of the condenser go into the movement of the charge. In this case, therefore, both mechanical and electrostatic energy are converted either into the chemical energy of the battery, or are expended in heating it.

100. (1) $C = \dfrac{(1 + \varepsilon)S}{8\pi d}$. (2) $E = \dfrac{2V}{d(1 + \varepsilon)}$; the field-strength is the same in air and in the liquid. (3) In air $\sigma = V/2\pi d(1 + \varepsilon)$; in liquid $\sigma' = \varepsilon V/2\pi d(1 + \varepsilon)$. (4) $\varDelta W = \dfrac{SV^2}{8\pi d} \dfrac{\varepsilon - 1}{\varepsilon + 1}$.

The energy $\varDelta W$ is used to do work in lifting the liquid between the condenser plates. The level of the liquid between the plates will be higher than in the vessel.

101. The change in the energy of the condenser is

(1) $\varDelta W_1 = \dfrac{(1 - \varepsilon)CV^2}{2} \approx -318$ erg,

(2) $\varDelta W_2 = \dfrac{(\varepsilon - 1)Q^2}{2C\varepsilon} \approx +1590$ erg.

The work done in removing the glass is $A_1 = +318$ erg; $A_2 = +1590$ erg.

Solution. In both cases, not only does the energy of the condenser change, but work is expended in removing the glass. This work is greater in the second case, since the field-strength in the condenser increases as the glass is withdrawn, whereas it remains fixed in the first case. In the first case, when the glass is removed, not only is mechanical work done, but the energy of the condenser is reduced and the energy of the source of e.m.f. is increased (see Problem 99). The work done against the e.m.f. of the source is $A = \Delta QV$, where ΔQ is the change in the charge on the condenser after removing the glass. Since $\Delta Q = (\varepsilon - 1)CV$, then $A = (\varepsilon - 1)CV^2$ and the work done in removing the plate is $A_1 = A + \Delta W_1 = \frac{1}{2}(\varepsilon - 1)CV^2$ $= +318$ erg. In the second case, when the glass is removed, mechanical work is done, equal to the increase in the energy of the condenser $A_2 = \Delta W_2 = +1590$ erg.

102. $M = \dfrac{nr^2V^2}{16\pi d} \approx 510$ dyne cm.

Solution. On turning the moving vanes of the condenser through $\Delta\varphi$, the charge on them is increased by ΔQ. The source performs the work $V\Delta Q$; this work goes into increasing the electrostatic energy of the condenser $\frac{1}{2}\Delta QV$ and into the work of the forces of attraction $M\Delta\varphi$. Thus

$$V\Delta Q = M\Delta\varphi + \frac{\Delta QV}{2}$$

or

$$M\Delta\varphi = \frac{\Delta QV}{2}. \qquad (1)$$

The increase in the charge is $\Delta Q = \Delta CV$, whilst the reduction in the capacity is

$$\Delta C = \frac{nr^2\Delta\varphi}{8\pi d}.$$

On substituting these expressions in (1) and cancelling $\Delta\varphi$, we obtain the answer.

103. $\alpha \approx 6\cdot5 \times 10^{-8}$ e.s.u.

§ 2. DIRECT CURRENT LAWS

104. $R = 0\cdot17$ ohm.

105. $W \approx 39\cdot5$ W.

106. $T = 2200\,°C.$

107. $R \approx 14\cdot4$ ohm, $\quad \alpha = 4\cdot5 \times 10^{-3}$ deg^{-1}.

108. $d \approx 5\cdot6$ mm.

109. $\dfrac{dT}{dt} = 0\cdot24 \dfrac{V^2}{\varrho \dfrac{4l}{\pi d^2} Mc} = 0\cdot0079$ degsec^{-1}.

110. $V_1 = \dfrac{72}{11}$ V; $\quad V_2 = \dfrac{36}{11}$ V; $\quad V_3 = \dfrac{24}{11}$ V.

111. $R = \dfrac{5}{11}r$.

112. See Fig. 162.

$$I = \frac{E}{R+r}; \tan\alpha = \frac{R^2}{E}.$$

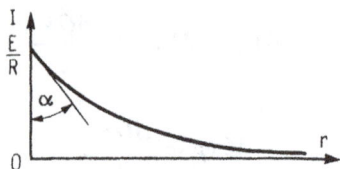

FIG. 162

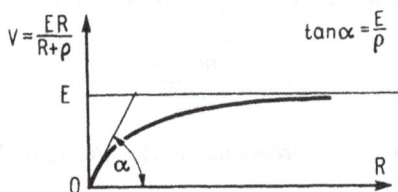

FIG. 163

113. See Fig. 163.

114. $E \approx 34\cdot3$ V; $\quad r \approx 1\cdot43$ ohm.

115. $R_{3v} = 1000$ ohm; $R_{15v} = 5000$ ohm; $R_{150v} = 50{,}000$ ohm

116. $dR/dI = -(R_{in} + \varrho + R)^2/E$, i.e. the greater R, the less the accuracy of the measurement. This formula gives the accuracy of the measurement of resistances by ordinary ohmmeters.

117. (1) The shunt resistance $r_{sh} \approx 8.1$ kOhm is calculated from the formula $1/r_{sh} = (1/a)(E/V - b) - 1/\varrho$, where $V = 0.125$ V is the voltage drop in the measuring instrument, $b = 1 + r_1/r_2$, $a = br_0 + r_1$.

(2) $E \approx 1.28$ V; this figure can be found from the formula in (1) with $r_{sh} = 22$ kOhm.

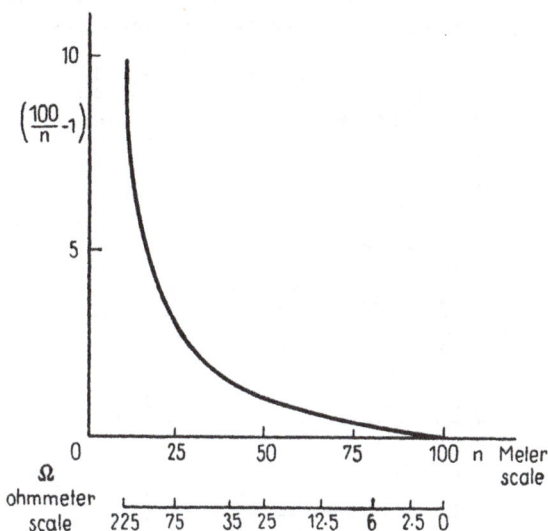

FIG. 164

(3) $r_x \approx 25 \left(\dfrac{100}{n} - 1 \right)$ ohm. The more general relationship is

$$r_x = (r_1 + R) \left(\frac{100}{n} - 1 \right), \quad \text{where} \quad \frac{1}{R} = \frac{1}{r_2} + \frac{1}{r_0 + \varrho_0} \quad \text{and}$$

$$\frac{1}{\varrho_0} = \frac{1}{\varrho} + \frac{1}{r_{sh}}.$$

A comparison of the scales of the instrument meter and the ohmmeter is shown in Fig. 164.

(4) $\Delta r_x \approx \dfrac{1250}{n^2}$ ohm is the error in determining the resistance

r_x, corresponding to a meter scale error of half a division when the needle reads n divisions. The minimum error when $n = 100$ is $\Delta r_x \approx 0 \cdot 125$ ohm, when $n = 5$, $\Delta r_x \approx 50$ ohm.

(5) $r_1 = 10$ ohm, $R = 240$ ohm (see section 3). Hence

$$r_2 \approx 325 \text{ ohm.}$$

118. $l_1/l_2 = 4$ (if the filaments are made of the same material and have the same temperature in the working conditions).

119. $x = \dfrac{r_2[Vr_3 - I(Rr_3 + Rr_4 + r_2r_4)]}{Vr_4 + I(Rr_3 + Rr_4 + r_2r_4 + r_3r_2 + r_3r_4)}$.

120. $R = \dfrac{7}{5}r$.

121. The relative error is

$$\frac{\Delta R_x}{R_x} = \frac{(R_x + R_3)(R_1 + R_2)}{R_2 R_x} \frac{\Delta V}{V},$$

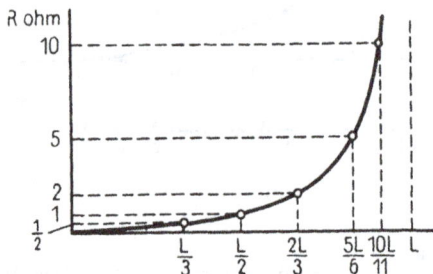

Fig. 165

where V is the voltage across the bridge and ΔV is the potential difference across the galvanometer terminals when changing R_x to $R_x + \Delta R_x$. At balance $R_x/R_3 = R_1/R_2 = b$, so that the factor multiplying $\Delta V/V$ will be $(1 + b)^2/b$; it has a minimum for $b = 1$.

122. The arm ratio required for bridge balance in one case also ensures balance in the other case. But the sensitivity of the bridge circuit depends on the ratios between the arm resistances and the internal resistances of the galvanometer and the source. The bridge sensitivity can thus vary (for example, see the answer to the previous problem).

123. See Fig. 165. The absolute error is $\Delta R = 10^{-3}/(1 - u)^2$ ohm, where $u = x/L$, x is the distance of the slider A from the left-hand end. The relative error is $\Delta R/R = 10^{-3}/u(1 - u)$; when $u = \frac{1}{2}$, it has a minimum of 4×10^{-3}. The absolute error increases to ∞ as $u \to 1$, i.e. as the measured resistance increases.

124. $I = \dfrac{E(R_2 + r)}{R_1 R_2 + (R_1 + R_2)r}$; $\cot \alpha = \dfrac{E}{R_1^2}$. See Fig. 166.

125. $R = 16\cdot7$ ohm.

126. $V = 1000$ V.

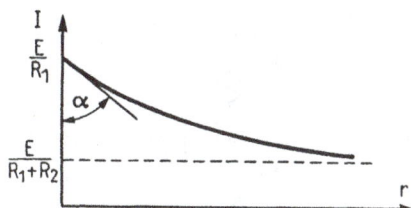

FIG. 166

127. (1) $V \approx 2\cdot93$ V, (2) $V = 2\cdot4$ V.

128. The circuit resistance is 1300 ohm, the internal resistance of the source is 325 ohm, the resistance of the second instrument is 13,260 ohm.

129. $i_1 \approx 1\cdot05$ amp (in the direction of the e.m.f.); $i_2 \approx 0\cdot87$ amp (opposite to the direction of the e.m.f.); $V \approx 1\cdot8$ V.

130. $I_0(r_i + R)$ V.

131. An additional resistance of 10^5 ohm is needed for the voltmeter. A shunt of $\approx 0\cdot1$ ohm is required for the ammeter.

132. (1) $I = \dfrac{E(R_1 + R_2)}{rR_1 + rR_2 + R_1 R_2}$, (2) $I_1 = \dfrac{ER_2}{rR_1 + rR_2 + R_1 R_2}$,

(3) $\dfrac{I_1^*}{I_1} = \dfrac{rR_1}{R_2(r + R_1)} + 1$, if $r \ll R$; then $\dfrac{I_1^*}{I_1} = n + 1$,

where $n = \dfrac{r}{R^2}$.

133. Use the circuit shown in Fig. 167, and take the resistances: $R_2 \approx 12 \cdot 2x$ ohm, and $R_1 \approx 61x/(1 + 0 \cdot 12x)$ ohm, where $x \leqslant 1$.

134. $i = 0 \cdot 75$ amp. The voltmeter indicates zero, since the voltage drop inside each element is equal to the e.m.f. of the element.

135. $0 \cdot 75$ V (on condition that the voltmeter resistance is sufficiently large).

136. Zero. See the answer to Problem 134.

137. $\dfrac{E'}{\varrho'} < \dfrac{E}{\varrho + R}$.

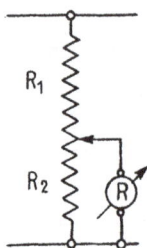

FIG. 167

138. Either when $r \ll R$ and $r \ll R_x$, or when $R_x \gg R$ (the internal resistance of the source obviously plays the same role as r).

139. $i = 10$ mamp.

140. $E_2(R + R_1) = E_1 R$.

141. $V_2 = 3$ V; $I_3 = 1$ amp.

142. $R_2 = 3$ ohm; R_1 and R_4 can have any values.

143. $V = \dfrac{E}{1 + \dfrac{(L - x)x}{L^2} \dfrac{R}{r}} \cdot \dfrac{x}{L}$, where x is the distance of the slider from the end of the rheochord, to which the voltmeter is joined.

144. $E = \dfrac{E_1 r_2 + E_2 r_1}{r_2 + r_1}$; $r = \dfrac{r_1 r_2}{r_2 + r_1}$. If $E_1 > E_2$, then $E_1 > E > E_2$ when $r_1 \neq 0$ and $r_2 \neq 0$.

145. $E = \dfrac{R_1 R_2 + R_1 R_3 + R_2 R_3}{R_2} I_3; \quad I_1 = \dfrac{R_2 + R_3}{R_2} I_3;$

$I_2 = \dfrac{R_3}{R_2} I_3.$

146. $E = \dfrac{I_4}{R_3 R_5} [R_1(R_2 R_5 + R_3 R_5 + R_4 R_5 + R_2 R_4 + R_3 R_4)$

$+ R_3(R_2 R_4 + R_2 R_5 + R_4 R_5)].$

147. $I_1 = 1\cdot64$ amp; $I_r = 2\cdot54$ amp; $I_2 = 2\cdot36$ amp;

$I_{r'} = 0\cdot18$ amp; $I_2' = 1\cdot82$ amp.

148. $E = 7\cdot75$ V.

149. $R_4 = \dfrac{V_{2,1}(R_1 R_2 + R_1 R_3 + R_2 R_3)}{R_2 R_3 I - V_{2,1}(R_2 + R_3)}.$

150. $\varrho = R - r.$

151. $C = \dfrac{r}{n[(R + r)(\varrho - r) + rR]} \approx 0\cdot0165 \,\mu\text{F}.$

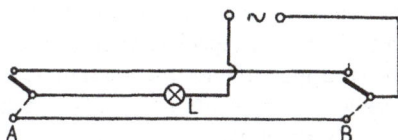

FIG. 168

152. If l denotes the length of the first section from the source of e.m.f. to the earthing point, L the total length of the line, ϱ the resistance per unit length of the line, I the current through the receiver, r the earthing resistance, i the current through the first section of the line, i_r the earthing current, E the e.m.f. at the start of the line, Kirchhoff's laws lead us to the equations $i = i_r + I$; $E = il\varrho + i_r r$; $i_r r = (L - l)\varrho I$. Hence $I = Er/(rL\varrho + \varrho^2 l(L - l))$. For I to be a minimum, $l(L - l)$ must be a maximum, as is the case when $l = L - l$, i.e. $l = \frac{1}{2}L$.

153. See Fig. 168. L is the lamp, A one end of the corridor and B the other end.

154. $r = \dfrac{\varrho}{2\pi l} \ln \dfrac{R_2}{R_1}$.

Solution. The field-strength E and current density j are connected by $E = \varrho j$. If the charge per unit length of the cylinder is σ, the field-strength round the cylinder is $E = 2\sigma/R$. Hence the potential difference between the cylinder walls is

$$V = 2\sigma \ln \frac{R_2}{R_1}.$$

By definition, the resistance $r = V/I$, where I is the current from one cylinder wall to the other. The current I can be written as $I = 2\pi R_1 l j_1$; on substituting in this $j_1 = 2\sigma/\varrho R_1$, we obtain $I = 4\pi l \sigma/\varrho$; on finding the ratio V/I, we get the answer.

155. $R = \dfrac{\varrho}{4\pi} \left(\dfrac{1}{r_2} - \dfrac{1}{r_1} \right)$.

156. We picture the electrostatic field between the conductors A and B when they are held at a definite potential difference V, the space between being empty. We compare this field with the electric field of force when the space between the conductors is filled with a uniform conducting medium (specific resistance ϱ) and the same potential difference is applied. Since the medium is uniform and the conductor surfaces are equipotential surfaces, the field-strength E must be the same in both cases.

In the case of the electrostatic field:

$$CV = e = \int \sigma \, dS,$$

where σ is the surface density of the charge on the element dS of surface, and the integration is over one of the conductor surfaces. Since $E = 4\pi\sigma$, we have

$$CV = \frac{1}{4\pi} \int E \, dS. \tag{1}$$

In the case of direct current:

$$\frac{V}{R} = I = \int j \, dS,$$

where j is the current density, and the integration is over the surface of the same conductor. Ohm's law gives, for all the points of the space, $E = j\varrho$. Consequently,

$$\frac{V}{R} = \frac{1}{\varrho} \int EdS. \tag{2}$$

On comparing (1) and (2), we get

$$R = \frac{\varrho}{4\pi C}.$$

157. $R = \dfrac{\varrho}{2\pi r}$.

Hint. Use the result of the previous problem and Problem 66.

158. $V_1 \approx 95 \text{ V}; \quad V_2 \approx 100 \text{ V}; \quad W_1 \approx 45 \text{ W}; \quad W_2 \approx 0 \cdot 1 \text{ W}.$

When the load resistance is doubled, in case (1) the current and power are almost halved; in case (2) the current is virtually unchanged whilst the power is doubled.

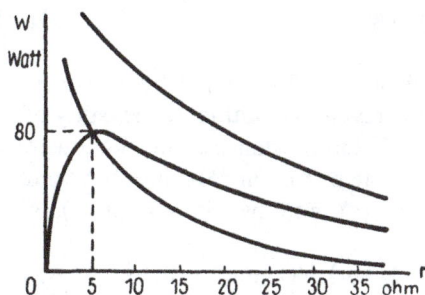

FIG. 169

159. $V_1 = 110 \text{ V}; \quad V_2 \approx 67 \text{ V}; \quad W_1 = 605 \text{ W}; \quad W_2 \approx 222 \text{ W}.$

When the load resistance is halved, V_1 is unchanged, V_2 falls to 50 V, W_1 is doubled, W_2 increases to 250 W.

160. See Fig. 169.

161. $I' = I \sqrt[3]{\dfrac{V'^2 W'}{V^2 W}}; \quad r' = r \sqrt[3]{\dfrac{W'^2 V^2}{W^2 V'^2}}.$

162. The voltage must be increased by $\frac{1}{2}p$ per cent.

163. $d = 3.3$ cm.

164. $s \approx \dfrac{2\varrho lN}{E^2 n} = 8.5$ mm^2, $d \approx 0.33$ cm.

165. $(100 + n)/10(1 + n)$ times.

166. (1) $m_D/m_0 = \frac{3}{8}$, where m_D is the weight of the conductors in system (a), m_0 the weight of conductors in the equivalent system (b).

Hint. The condition for the same powers gives $EI_0 = 2EI$, or $I_0 = 2I$, where $I = I_1 = I_2$. We obtain from the condition for the

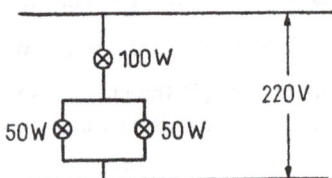

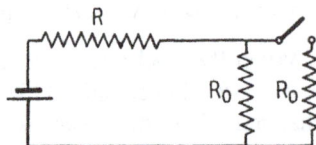

FIG. 170   FIG. 171

same consumed power: $R = 2R_0$, where $R = R_1 = R_2$. Taking into account the previous condition, the equality of the losses gives $r = 4r_0$, where r is the resistance of one conductor in system (a), r_0 the same for system (b). On recalling that there are three conductors in system (a), and two in system (b), we arrive at the answer.

(2) $N_0/N_D = (1 + \alpha)^2/4(1 + \alpha^2 - \alpha)$, where N_0 is the loss in the ordinary circuit (b), and N_D is the loss in the Dolivo-Dobrovol'skii system. When $\alpha = 1$ the loss ratio is a minimum, so that a small mismatch in practice does not produce an increase in the loss in the equivalent circuit (b).

Hint. The condition for the generators to have the same power is $EI_0 = E(I_1 + I_2)$, and the relationship for the conductor resistances obtained in (1), yield all that is necessary for the solution.

167. See Fig. 170.

168. The power consumed by the first bulb decreases by 1.4 W, and that by the second by 2.1 W.

169. See Fig. 171. $R = R_0/\sqrt{2}$.

170. $T - T_0 = \dfrac{RI^2}{2\pi rlk} (1 - e^{-\frac{2kt}{rcd}})$.

171. $T = \dfrac{V^2 + kST_0R_0}{kSR_0 - V^2\alpha}$.

172. $W = \dfrac{V^2}{R_0} \left\{ 1 + \dfrac{\alpha}{1 - \alpha T_1} \right.$

$$\times [T_0 + T_1 - T_1 (1 + \alpha T_0) e^{-\frac{mct}{kS(1-\alpha T_1)}}] \Bigg\},$$

where $T_1 = V^2/kSR_0$ and k is the coefficient in Newton's law.

§ 3. PERMANENT MAGNETS

173. The needles are parallel to the opposite sides of the triangle (Fig. 172a), this being a position of stable equilibrium. An equi-

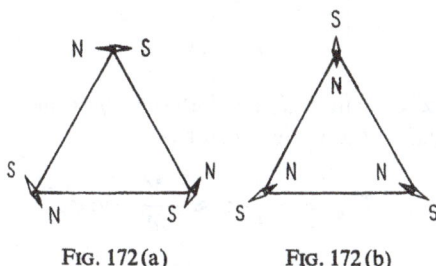

FIG. 172(a)   FIG. 172(b)

librium is also obtained when the needles are at right angles to the opposite sides (Fig. 172(b)), but this position is not stable.

174. $V = -\dfrac{M \cos \varphi}{\mu d^2}$;

$$H = \dfrac{M}{\mu d^3} \sqrt{1 + 3 \cos^2 \varphi}; \quad \theta = \arctan \left(\frac{1}{2} \tan \varphi \right).$$

Solution. Let $M = ml$, where l is the distance between two magnetic poles m. The potential at the point A (Fig. 173) is now

$$V = -\frac{m}{\mu\left(d - \dfrac{l}{2}\cos\varphi\right)} + \frac{m}{\mu\left(d + \dfrac{l}{2}\cos\varphi\right)} \approx -\frac{ml\cos\varphi}{\mu d^2}$$

$$= -\frac{M}{\mu d^2}\cos\varphi$$

on condition that $l \ll d$.

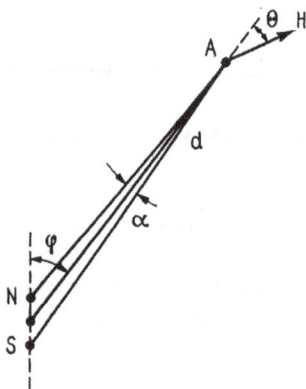

FIG. 173

The angle $\alpha \approx (l\sin\varphi)/d$, so that the component of the field-strength normal to the radius vector is

$$H_\perp \approx \frac{m}{\mu d^2}\alpha \approx \frac{M}{\mu d^3}\sin\varphi,$$

discounting magnitudes of order l/d. The component along the radius vector is given to the same accuracy by

$$H_\| \approx \frac{m}{\mu}\left[\frac{1}{\left(d - \dfrac{l}{2}\cos\varphi\right)^2} - \frac{1}{\left(d + \dfrac{l}{2}\cos\varphi\right)^2}\right] \approx \frac{2M}{\mu d^3}\cos\varphi.$$

Hence,

$$H = \sqrt{H_\perp^2 + H_\|^2} \quad \text{and} \quad \tan\Theta = \frac{H_\perp}{H_\|}.$$

175. $E_{pot} = -MH \cos \theta.$

176. $F = \dfrac{m^2}{(n-1)^2 l^2} + \dfrac{m^2}{(n+1)^2 l^2} - \dfrac{2m^2}{n^2 l^2} \approx \dfrac{m^2}{l^2} \dfrac{(6n^2-1)}{n^6}$

$$\approx \frac{6}{n^4} \left(\frac{M}{l^2}\right)^2,$$

where $m = M/l$ is the magnetic pole-strength.

177. $T \approx \dfrac{\pi}{10M} \sqrt{Il^3}.$

178. Since the moment of the restoring force increases as a result of the increase in the arm of this force, the period of vibration diminishes.

179. $H = \dfrac{3mgl}{8M} \approx 450$ oersted, $\quad T = 2\pi l \sqrt{\dfrac{2m}{3mgl - 6MH}}.$

The direction of H is opposite to that of M.

180. $T = \pi l \sqrt{\dfrac{P}{3gMH}}.$

181. The rod forms an angle α with the plane of the magnetic meridian, given by $C(\alpha - \alpha_0) = MH \sin \alpha$, where α_0 is the angle at which the thread is not twisted, measured from the plane of the magnetic meridian, and C is the coefficient of torsional elasticity of the thread. The rod forms an angle β with the vertical given by

$$\tan \beta = \frac{pR + HM}{MH_V}.$$

182. $H_0 = 0.8$ oersted.

183. The field H is produced by surface magnetic charge of density $\sigma = I$ (Fig. 174(a)). The field B is shown in Fig. 174(b). Outside, the fields B and H are the same. The interior field $B = -H + 4\pi I$ and is in the same direction as I.

184. $M = \dfrac{\pi^2 m l^2}{3T^2 H} \approx 24$ e.m.u.

185. $H = 6260$ oersted, $\sigma = 550$ e.m.u.

Hint. The force $F = 2\pi\sigma^2 S$, whilst the field in the gap is $H = 4\pi\sigma$.

186. Two equilibrium positions are possible:

(1)   ↑ ↑   ↑ ↑   is unstable.

(2)   → →   → →   is stable.

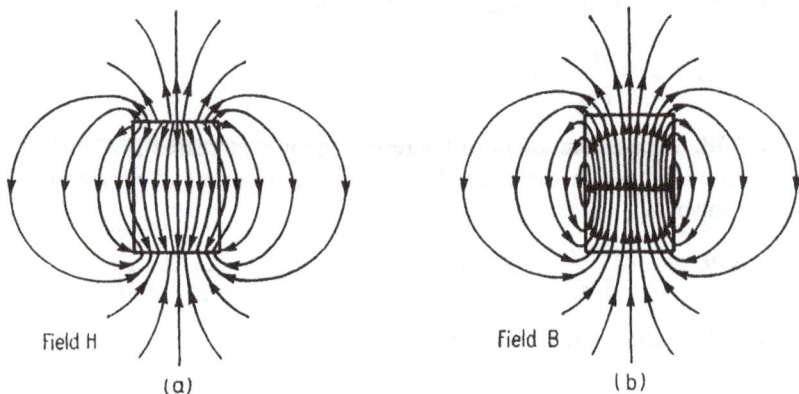

Field H   Field B

(a)   (b)

FIG. 174

187. $H = \dfrac{2\pi}{Td}\sqrt{\dfrac{2I \tan\alpha}{d}}$.

188. $M = \dfrac{\pi d}{T}\sqrt{\dfrac{2Id}{\tan\alpha}}$.

§4. THE MAGNETIC FIELD OF A CURRENT

189. It is increased four times.

190. Perpendicular to the plane of the loop: at the point A towards the observer, and at the point B away from the observer.

191. Inside the pipe $H = 0$, outside the pipe $H = 2I/r$, where r is the distance from the axis.

192. Inside the conductor $H = 2Ir/R^2$, outside $H = 2I/r$.

193. $H = \dfrac{2I}{r}$ (1 + cos α), where r is the distance from the point A; the direction of H is perpendicular to the conductor carrying the current $2I$.

194. $H = \dfrac{I}{r}\sqrt{6 + 4(\cos α + \cos β) + 2\cos(α + β)},$

where r is the distance from the point A. The vector H forms an angle

$$\varphi = \arctan\frac{\sin α - \sin β}{2 + \cos α + \cos β}$$

with the plane perpendicular to the conductor carrying the current $2I$.

195. The magnetic field vector lies in the plane of symmetry. Along the line AO the field is perpendicular to this line and has the value

$$H = 2(\sqrt{2} - 1)\frac{I}{r};$$

along the line AO' the field has the value

$$H = 2(\sqrt{2} + 1)\frac{I}{r};$$

along the line perpendicular to the plane of the currents and passing through the point A,

$$H = \sqrt{2}\frac{I}{r},$$

where r is the distance from the point A.

The magnetic field lines will be closest together round the line $O'A$ and are correspondingly furthest apart round the line AO. The path of the lines is illustrated roughly in Fig. 175.

196. $H = 0$.

197. $H = \dfrac{8I}{ab}\sqrt{a^2 + b^2}.$

198. $H = \dfrac{18I}{a}$.

199. $H = 0$.

200. $H = 0$.

201. The field strength is

$$H = \frac{4\pi I}{R} \left(\sin 15° + \sin 45° + \sin 75° \right) \approx \frac{7\cdot73\pi I}{R}$$

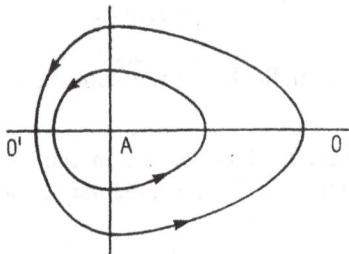

FIG. 175

is directed away from the plane of the figure and forms an angle $\alpha = 15°$ with the plane of the first turn (angles are reckoned clockwise when viewed from above).

202. The field strength is

$$H = \frac{16I}{hD} \sqrt{h^2 + D^2} \left(\sin \frac{\pi}{8} + \sin \frac{3\pi}{8} \right) \approx \frac{20\cdot9I}{hD} \sqrt{h^2 + D^2}$$

and forms an angle $22° 30'$ with the plane of the turn AB (angles are reckoned counter-clockwise).

203. Inside the sphere the field corresponds to the field of a straight infinitely long conductor carrying a current I, whilst the field is zero outside the sphere.

Hint. We can conclude from arguments based on the rotational symmetry and the fact that the lines of force are closed that the latter can only be circles lying in the plane perpendicular to AB. If we use this fact and apply the law $\oint H \, ds = 4\pi \sum I$, we obtain the answer.

204. $H = \dfrac{\pi I(N + 1)}{R}$.

Hint. $\sum\limits_{n=1}^{N} \sin^2 \dfrac{\pi n}{2N} = \dfrac{1}{2}(N + 1)$.

205. $H = 0$.

206. $H = \dfrac{4I}{R}\left(\arcsin \dfrac{a}{R} + \dfrac{\sqrt{R^2 - a^2}}{a}\right)$.

207. $H = \dfrac{2\pi I N \ln(R/r)}{R - r}$.

Hint. The field dH produced by the current element $I dl$ is $I d\varphi/\varrho$, where ϱ is the distance of the element from the centre of the spiral,

$$\varrho = r + \dfrac{R - r}{2\pi N}\varphi.$$

208. $H = \dfrac{2\pi N I}{l}(\cos \beta - \cos \alpha)$.

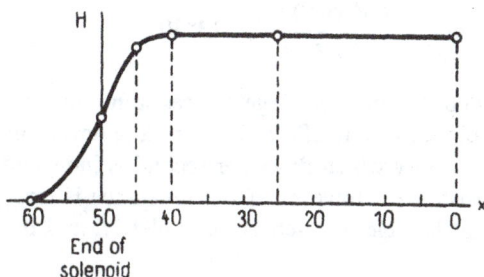

FIG. 176

209. $H \approx 12\cdot56$; $12\cdot56$; $12\cdot56$; $12\cdot44$; $6\cdot28$; $0\cdot25$. See Fig. 176.

210. $H = 2\pi I R^2\{[R^2 + (R + x)^2]^{-3/2} + [R^2 + (x - R)^2]^{-3/2}\}$, x is the distance from the centre of symmetry (see Fig. 177).

$$a \approx R\left(1 - \dfrac{2}{25\sqrt{5}}\right); \quad b \approx \dfrac{2\cdot2\pi I}{R}; \quad c = \dfrac{\pi I \sqrt{2}}{R}.$$

Hint. When determining $a = R - \varepsilon$ the expression for the derivative has to be expanded in powers of the small quantity ε/R.

211. Perpendicular to the axis of the current,

$$F = \frac{k}{D} mH \frac{dH}{dx} = \frac{3\pi^2 kmI^2}{4DR^3} \approx 1{\cdot}1 \times 10^{-7} \text{ dyne.}$$

where H is the magnetic field and x the distance from the centre of the circle.

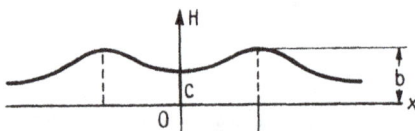

Fig. 177

Hint. The magnetic moment of the rod is $M = -kmH/D$; the force acting on a magnetised body in a non-uniform field is

$$F = -M \frac{dH}{dx}.$$

212. $\alpha = \arctan \dfrac{\pi CVNn\,10^{-6}}{5aH} = 13°30'.$

213. Provided it is not too large, the resistance in the condenser–inclinometer circuit has no effect on the needle deviation, since the amount of electricity which flows per second is independent of the size of the resistance. However, if the resistance is large, the condenser may not be able to discharge completely, and the deviation will be less.

214. $\varrho = \dfrac{r \tan \alpha_1 - R \tan \alpha_2}{\tan \alpha_2 - \tan \alpha_1} = 3{\cdot}7$ ohm.

215. $I = k \dfrac{\tan \theta + \tan \theta'}{\sqrt{4 + (\tan \theta - \tan \theta')^2}}.$

Hint. The forces acting on the ends of the needle in the two cases are represented by OB and OA in Fig. 178, where OO' is the plane of the current; the earth's field is directed along OC. $AC = CB$ and $OC \times I = CB \times k$.

216. Less than two amperes, since $I = 2 \sin \theta$ amp.

217. (1) $I' = \dfrac{IR'}{2R} (\cot \theta - \cot \theta')$; (2) $H = \dfrac{\pi I}{R} (\cot \theta + \cot \theta')$.

218. $I = \dfrac{HRR'}{2\pi(R \cot \theta - R')}$.

219. $I = \dfrac{D\theta}{HSn \cos \theta}$.

220. The accuracy is about 1 per cent.

221. The moment of the couple $M = 4I_0SI$; it is directed along the diagonal AC.

222. (1) The conductor is attracted to the magnet with a force $F = \dfrac{2\pi I_0 SIR^2}{(d^2 + R^2)^{3/2}}$, (2) the conductor is stretched along the radius with a force $f = \dfrac{I_0 SId}{(d^2 + R^2)^{3/2}}$ per unit length.

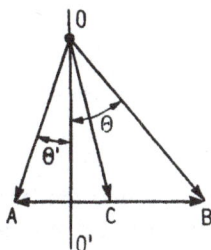

FIG. 178

223. $W = 4 \times 10^{-8} HSIn$ joule.

224. (1) $M = mI(2 - \sqrt{2})$, (2) $x = I(\sqrt{2} - 1)$.

225. $\omega = \dfrac{H}{20} \dfrac{E}{Rk} (1 - e^{-\frac{3kt}{m}})$, where $k = \alpha + \dfrac{H^2I^2}{4R} \times 10^{-9}$.

226. (1) $\alpha \approx 12° 15'$, (2) $I = 4 \cdot 7 \times 10^{-7}$ amp.

227. In the equilibrium position the plane of the frame is perpendicular to the direction of the external field. When the direction of the magnetic field produced by the current coincides with the direction of the external field the equilibrium is stable; when these directions are opposite to one another the equilibrium is unstable.

228. (1) Clockwise when viewed in the direction of the field;

(2) $T = 2\pi \sqrt{\dfrac{I_0}{a^2 niH}}$.

229. $\Phi = \dfrac{0.4Na^2\mu I}{D} = 32{,}000$ maxwell.

230. $\Phi = \dfrac{0.4\pi Na^2\mu I}{\pi D + (\mu - 1)d} \approx 24{,}000$ maxwell.

231. $\mu = \dfrac{\pi D(\Phi_1 - \Phi_2)}{\Phi_2 d_2 - \Phi_1 d_1} + 1 = 315$.

232. When the coils are connected in parallel (ends 1–3 and 2–4 joined) the lifting force is four times greater.

233. $F \approx 5$ kg.

234. $I \approx 6.5$ amp.

235. $I = \sqrt{\dfrac{PL}{0.4\pi nNS}}$.

236. A substantial reduction in the length of the coil leads to a reduction in the load P, since the magnetic field-strength of the coil is decreased by shortening its length.

237. The value of an alternating current can be measured provided the period of the current is much less than the period of vibration of the balance. The device will indicate the effective value of the current.

238. The device will measure power if the long coil with the greater number of turns is connected in parallel with the load, and the short coil with the small number of turns in series with the load. The moment of the force acting on the beam will be proportional to the product of the forces due to the currents flowing in the coils, i.e. is proportional to the power delivered to the load.

239. $p = 2\pi I^2 n^2$.

Solution. The force acting on a current element Idl in a magnetic field is $I\,dl\,H$, where H is the "effective magnetic field". The effective field means in this case the field-strength produced at the given point by all the elements of current flowing in the solenoid with the exception of the element being considered. The effective field can be found as follows. Inside a long solenoid the field close to the current element $I\,dl$ is made up of the field H produced by all the current elements except the one considered and the field H' produced by the element considered. The sum of these two fields of the same direction is equal to $4\pi nI$, i.e. $H + H' = 4\pi nI$. Outside the long solenoid the sum of these fields is zero close to the element considered because the field H' reverses its direction, i.e. $H - H' = 0$. We obtain from these two equations $H = 2\pi nI$, whence the force acting on the current element is $2\pi I^2 n\,dl$, and the required pressure is $p = 2\pi I^2 n^2$.

240. The spatial electric charge is zero in conductors carrying current, since the number of electrons is the same as the number of positive ions. Electric charge can only be present on the surfaces of the conductors, and the amount is small provided the potential difference is not very large; thus the forces of interaction between the surface charges are insignificant. The magnetic forces are therefore predominant, i.e. the forces of interaction between the moving charges, and they produce attraction when the current directions are the same. The spatial electric charge is not zero in cathode rays (since only electrons are present), and the predominant forces of interaction are those of repulsion between like charges; the magnetic fields of cathode rays are weak.

241. See Fig. 179. The electric lines of force are shown dotted. The magnetic lines of force are continuous. In the left-hand conductor the current travels from the observer into the figure. It travels from the figure towards the observer in the right-hand conductor.

Use the answer to Problem 17 for drawing the graph.

242. There is no electric field since there is no potential difference between corresponding points of the conductors. The magnetic field is illustrated in Fig. 180. At the point A the magnetic field is zero; remote from A the field has cylindrical symmetry and corresponds to a straight current of twice the size.

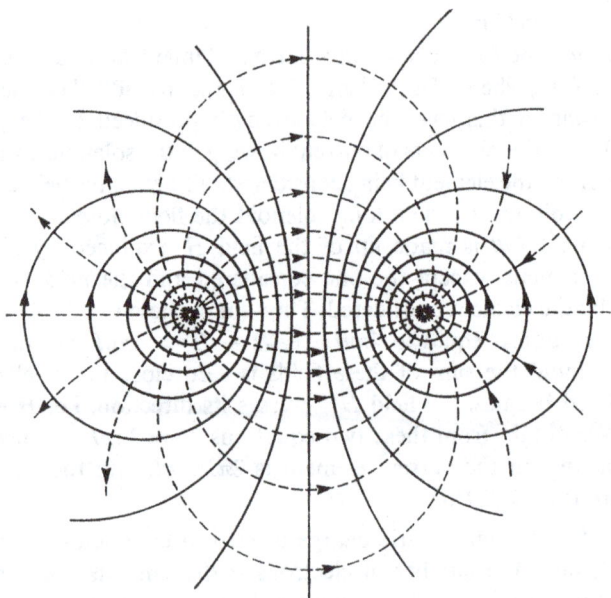

Fig. 179

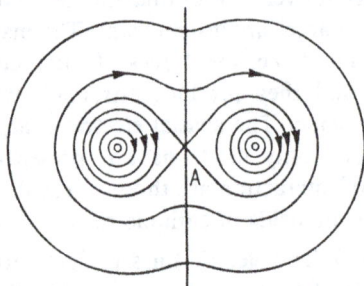

Fig. 180

243. The equilibrium position is at a distance $d = 0.02Iil/P$, but it is unstable, and the wire either falls or is attracted to the pin.

244. The first case: the currents I and i are in the same direction. The force of mutual attraction between the pin and the wire at a distance x cm is $F = 0.02Iil/x$ dyne. The resultant of the gravity force and the elastic forces of the springs is directed downwards and is $f = 2k(h - x)$ dyne. In the equilibrium position $F = f$.

Hence

$$x_1 = \frac{h}{2} + \sqrt{\frac{h^2}{4} - \frac{0.01 Iil}{k}}$$

(stable equilibrium),

$$x_2 = \frac{h}{2} - \sqrt{\frac{h^2}{4} - \frac{0.01 Iil}{k}}$$

(unstable equilibrium). If $h^2/4 \ll 0.01 Iil/k$ or $k < 0.04 Iil/h^2$, the wire is attracted to the pin.

The second case: the currents I and i are in opposite directions. The wire is repelled and will be at a distance

$$x = \frac{h}{2} + \sqrt{\frac{h^2}{4} + \frac{0.01 Iil}{k}}$$

in stable equilibrium.

245. A difference between the liquid levels in the vertical tubes is established; in the right-hand tube (viewing from the north pole) the liquid is higher.

246. $i = \dfrac{hd\varrho g}{B}$. The sensitivity is proportional to B and inversely proportional to d and ϱ.

247. It falls by $h = H^2\varkappa/2dg$ if $\varkappa < 0$, and rises by h if $\varkappa > 0$.

§ 5. ELECTROMAGNETIC INDUCTION

248. When the bridge moves an e.m.f. E_i and current I_i are obtained, and work E_iI_i is done in unit time. This power comes from the work of the external force F, i.e. $E_iI_i = Fv$, where v is the speed with which the bridge moves. On the other hand, the force acting on the bridge due to the presence of the current I in the magnetic field of induction B is equal to $F_1 = BIl$, where l is the length of the bridge. If $I = I_i$, by Lenz's law $F_1 = -F$. Hence $E_i = -Blv$. Since the change in the flux of induction Φ crossing the circuit, when the bridge moves a distance dx, is $d\Phi = Bl\,dx$, we have $Blv = d\Phi/dt$. Finally, $E_i = -d\Phi/dt$, which is in fact the law of induction.

249. 1 mV in each case.

250. It will be the curved path inclined to the horizontal.

251. $E = 2Iab \dfrac{v}{x(x + a)}$, where x is the distance between the frame and the wire. If the wire is vertical and the current in it travels from bottom to top, a clockwise current is produced in the frame when it moves away from the wire.

252. No, since the field round the frame is non-uniform.

253. $E = H_0ab[\omega \sin \omega t \cos (\omega't - \varphi) + \omega' \cos \omega t \sin (\omega't - \varphi)]$.

(1) $E = H_0ab\omega \sin 2\omega t$ for $\varphi = 0$;

(2) $E = H_0ab\omega \cos 2\omega t$ for $\varphi = -\dfrac{\pi}{2}$.

254. $E = Hab\omega \sin \omega_0 \left(t - \dfrac{1 - e^{-kt}}{k} \right)$.

255. $\varkappa = \dfrac{E_1 - E_2}{4\pi E_2} \approx 13 \times 10^{-5}$.

256. (1) $I \approx 1\cdot2$ amp. (2) The current would rise to 240 amp, and the winding would overheat.

257. $I = 0\cdot314$ amp.

258. The current remains as before, $0\cdot314$ amp.

259. $R = 4\pi nN\omega S$.

260. (1) $N \approx 1$ rev/sec, (2) it must be increased $\varrho_{\text{iron}}/\varrho_{\text{copper}}$ times, i.e. 5·06 times.

261. If the rod axis is taken as the z axis, the electric lines of force lie in planes perpendicular to the z axis, and form concentric circles with centres on the z axis (Fig. 181). The magnitude of the field-strength vector E is inversely proportional to the distance from the z axis.

262. (1) A direct current $I = -(1/R) \, d\Phi/dt$, where Φ is the flux of induction in the rod. (2) If the flux in the rod is directed from top to bottom, the current in the turn is counter-clockwise when viewed from above.

263. It will describe an untwisting spiral with ever-increasing velocity about the rod.

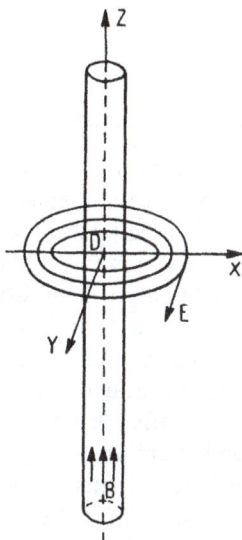

FIG. 181

264. (1) $L = 0.25$ H, (2) $N = 250$.

265. It is necessary to measure the current I and the magnetic field-strength H inside the coil, to determine the cross-sectional area S and number of turns N. The magnetic flux through the coil is then $\Phi = HSN = LI$, whence $L = HSN/I$.

266. 0.24×10^{-6} H.

Hint. The magnetic field-strength inside the tube at a distance r from its axis is $H = 2I/r$ (we neglect edge effects). Outside the tube there is no magnetic field. Hence the flux through the radial partition is $\Phi = 2Il \int_{r_0}^{r_1} dr/r$, where l is the length of the tube, r_0

is the radius of the wire, r_1 the inner radius of the tube. We have $L = 2 \ln r_1/r_0$ per unit length.

267. $L \approx 4 \ln d/r \approx 9.2 \times 10^{-9}$ H.

268. $M = \sqrt{L_1 L_2} = 0.6$ H.

269. (1) L is close to 0, (2) $L = 0.2$ H, (3) $L = 0.05$ H.

270. $W = \dfrac{2\pi N^2 S I^2}{l}$.

271. (1) 8 ln 2 erg, (2) it is increased by 8 ln 2 erg.

272. Since the conductors are repelled, as they move apart, e.m.f.'s opposed to the flow of the currents must be produced in them, by virtue of Lenz's law. Consequently, in order to maintain the currents unchanged, additional e.m.f.'s in the same direction as the currents must be brought into circuit whilst the conductors are moving. The work of these e.m.f.'s in fact goes into performing the mechanical work and increasing the magnetic energy of the system. If additional e.m.f.'s are not brought into the circuit, the current in the conductors will be less after they have been moving for a time Δt than when the conductors are fixed. The work $\mathcal{E}I\Delta t$ done by the e.m.f.'s maintaining the currents in the conductors is similarly reduced. The amount of heat $RI^2\Delta t$ released in the conductors is still further reduced. As a result of this "economy" in the Joule heat, mechanical work is done and the magnetic energy of the system is increased.

273. $I_0 = \dfrac{E}{L} t$, where r is the time from the instant of switching on. But when the current increases substantially, even a small ohmic resistance in the circuit will play an essential role. Due to the presence of resistance the growth of the current is slowed down, then ceases altogether.

274. (1) $a = \dfrac{mg}{m + CH^2 l^2}$, (2) $I = \dfrac{mgHlC}{m + CH^2 l^2}$.

275. $x = \dfrac{mgL}{H^2 l^2}(1 - \cos \omega t)$, where $\omega = \dfrac{Hl}{\sqrt{mL}}$.

276. The velocity will increase until the force of interaction between the induced current and the magnetic field reaches a value equal to the weight of the conductor. This occurs at the value

$$v_{st} = PR/H^2l^2.$$

277. The logarithmic decrement increases

$$\Delta = \frac{\left(k + \dfrac{H^2l^3}{4R}\right)\sqrt{\dfrac{g}{l} - \left(\dfrac{k}{2ml}\right)^2}}{k\sqrt{\dfrac{g}{l} - \left(\dfrac{k + \dfrac{H^2l^3}{4R}}{2ml}\right)^2}} \text{ times.}$$

278. The logarithmic decrement and the period increase

$$\Delta = \frac{\sqrt{\dfrac{g}{l} - \left(\dfrac{k}{2ml}\right)^2}}{\sqrt{\dfrac{g}{l} + \dfrac{H^2l^2}{4mL} - \left(\dfrac{k}{2ml}\right)^2}} \text{ times.}$$

279. The logarithmic decrement diminishes

$$\sqrt{\frac{\dfrac{g}{l}\left(1 + \dfrac{CH^2l^2}{4m}\right) - \left(\dfrac{k}{2ml}\right)^2}{\dfrac{g}{l} - \left(\dfrac{k}{2ml}\right)^2}} \text{ times.}$$

and the period is increased

$$\frac{\left(1 + \dfrac{CH^2l^2}{4m}\right)\sqrt{\dfrac{g}{l} - \left(\dfrac{k}{2ml}\right)^2}}{\sqrt{\dfrac{g}{l}\left(1 + \dfrac{CH^2l^2}{4m}\right) - \left(\dfrac{k}{2ml}\right)^2}} \text{ times.}$$

280. (1) The logarithmic decrement is increased

$$\frac{\left(k + \dfrac{H^2 S^2}{R}\right)\sqrt{4IC - k^2}}{k\sqrt{4IC - \left(k + \dfrac{H^2 S^2}{R}\right)^2}} \text{ times.}$$

Here k is the coefficient of the moment of the friction forces, S is the area of the ring, I the moment of inertia of the ring, C the coefficient of torsion of the thread.

(2) The damping will be the same as when the magnetic field is absent.

281. The period is reduced by ΔT, where

$$\frac{\Delta T}{T} = \frac{T^2 S^2 H^2}{8\pi^2 LI},$$

if we regard ΔT as small compared with T.

282. The damping decrement of the ring is reduced

$$\sqrt{1 + \frac{4H^2 S^2 I}{L(4IC - k^2)}} \text{ times.}$$

283. $Q = \dfrac{\Delta \Phi}{R} = \dfrac{SIb \ln\left(\dfrac{d + a}{d - a}\right)}{(a + b)\varrho}.$

284. It is not affected, since the current in the frame before and after rotation is zero. In fact, by Kirchhoff's law, $-d\Phi/dt = RI + LdI/dt$. Hence $\Delta\Phi = R\displaystyle\int_0^t I\,dt + L(I_{end} - I_{start})$, but $I_{end} = I_{start} = 0$. Consequently $\Delta\Phi = RQ$.

285. It will. In fact, we have for this case

$$\int_0^{T/2} I\,dt = \int_0^{T/2} \frac{(\Phi_0 - \Phi)\,dt}{L},$$

since $LdI = d\Phi$. The integral on the right-hand side depends on the speed of rotation.

286. $\Delta\Phi = 2000$ maxwell.

287. The time taken to remove the plate must be very small compared with the period of the galvanometer.

288. The time constant $\tau = L/R$ of the circuit must be much less than the galvanometer period.

289. $\gamma = \dfrac{SNH \sin 30°}{(R+R')q} = 5$ divisions.

290. $I = \dfrac{\pi R^2 B}{L}$, where L is the inductance of the ring.

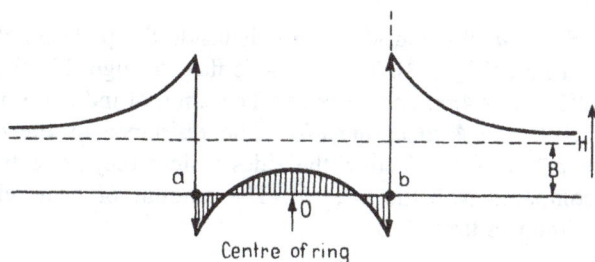

FIG. 182

291. (1) Zero, (2) $H = 2\pi^2 RB/L$, (3) see Fig. 182.

292. $H = 0$; $I = 0$.

293. $A = \dfrac{\pi^2 R^4 B^2}{2L}$.

294. $M = CR_1 R_2$.

Solution. On applying Kirchhoff's law to the circuit containing the galvanometer G, we can write

$$M\dot{I}_1 = R_2 I_2 + R_g I,$$

where I_1 is the current in the circuit of the source E prior to closing the switch, I_2 is the discharge current through R_2, I is the current through the galvanometer (R_g is the galvanometer resistance). Hence,

$$\int M\dot{I}_1 dt = R_2 \int I_2 dt + \int R_g I dt.$$

But $\int I_1 dt = I_1;$ $\int R_2 I_2 \, dt = R_2 Q = R_2 R_1 I_1 C;$ $\int R_g I \, dt = 0.$
Thus $MI_1 = R_2 R_1 I_1 C$ and hence $M = R_2 R_1 C.$

295. $M = \left(C + c \dfrac{\theta}{\theta + \theta'} \right) R_1 R_2.$

296. $Q = 0.24 \dfrac{4\pi^5 N^4 f^2 D^3 ah}{10^{18} \varrho H^2} \cdot I_{\text{eff}}^2 \approx 6.85$ kcal.

297. $Q = 0.24 \dfrac{\pi^5 N^4 D^4 a f^2 I_{\text{eff}}^2}{10^{18} \cdot 2\varrho H^2} \approx 35$ kcal.

298. *Solution.* We consider a circuit inside the plate parallel to its lateral face (Fig. 183). The magnetic flux through this circuit is $\Phi = BNS = \mu \times 4\pi n I_0 \cos \omega t \times bx.$ The e.m.f. of induction in this circuit is $E = \mu \, 4\pi n I_0 \omega \sin \omega t \, bx.$ The resistance of the circuit is $R_x = \varrho \, 2b/l \, dx$ (neglecting the sides x since they are extremely small compared with the sides b). The amount of heat released in this circuit in time dt is

$$dQ = 0.24 \frac{E_x^2}{R} dt = 0.24 \frac{(\mu \, 4\pi n I_0 \omega \sin \omega t \, bx)^2}{\varrho \, 2b} b \, dx \, dt.$$

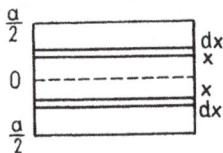

FIG. 183

Hence the amount of heat released per second in the plate is

$$Q = 0.24 \frac{(\mu \, 4\pi n \omega b I_{\text{eff}})^2 l}{2\varrho b} \int_0^{a/2} x^2 \, dx = 0.24 \frac{\mu^2 \pi^2 n^2 \omega^2 a^3 b I_{\text{eff}}^2}{3\varrho}$$

$$= 0.6 \text{ cal.}$$

299. $\dfrac{W_1}{W_2} = \dfrac{12a^2 b^2}{(a + b)^2 d^2}.$

300. (1) $I = \dfrac{NSH\omega}{\sqrt{\left(\dfrac{1}{C\omega} - L\omega\right)^2 + R^2}} \sin(\omega t + \varphi)$,

where

$$\tan\varphi = \dfrac{\dfrac{1}{C\omega} - L\omega}{R}; \quad V = \dfrac{NSH\omega \cos(\omega t + \varphi)}{\sqrt{(1 - LC\omega^2)^2 + R^2\omega^2 C^2}};$$

(2) $LC\omega^2 = 1$,   (3) $Q = 0.24 \dfrac{N^2 S^2 H^2 \omega^2}{2R \times 10^{16}} = 4.8 \times 10^{-10}$ kcal.

Hint. Kirchhoff's equations for the coil circuit are

$$L\dfrac{d^2 I}{dt^2} + R\dfrac{dI}{dt} + \dfrac{I}{C} = NSH\omega^2 \cos\omega t,$$

$$LC\dfrac{d^2 V}{dt^2} + RC\dfrac{dV}{dt} + V = NSH\omega \sin\omega t.$$

The stationary values of I and V are obtained as particular solutions of these equations.

301. (1) $V = \dfrac{NSH\omega}{2} e^{-\frac{2t}{RC}}$,

(2) $Q = 0.24 \dfrac{N^2 S^2 H^2 \omega}{8R \times 10^{16}} = 12 \times 10^{-10}$ kcal.

302. The magnetic needle performs harmonic vibrations relative to its equilibrium position in the magnetic meridian. When the horizontal copper disc is brought up from below, Foucault currents are produced in it, which brake the needle vibrations. In these circumstances the differential equation of the motion of the needle is

$$I\ddot{\alpha} = -HM\alpha - \eta\dot{\alpha},$$

where H is the horizontal component of the earth's magnetic field and η is the coefficient of proportionality of the braking force. The equation can be rewritten as

$$I\ddot{\alpha} + \eta\dot{\alpha} + HM\alpha = 0.$$

The motion is aperiodic when $\eta^2 = 4IHM$ or $\eta = 2\sqrt{IHM}$. The copper disc, rotating with angular velocity ω, will therefore act on the needle with a moment $M_e = 2\sqrt{IMH}\,\omega$. (1) This means that the needle will not move if a moment of the same size but opposite direction is exerted on the needle. (2) Since the needle does not move, the

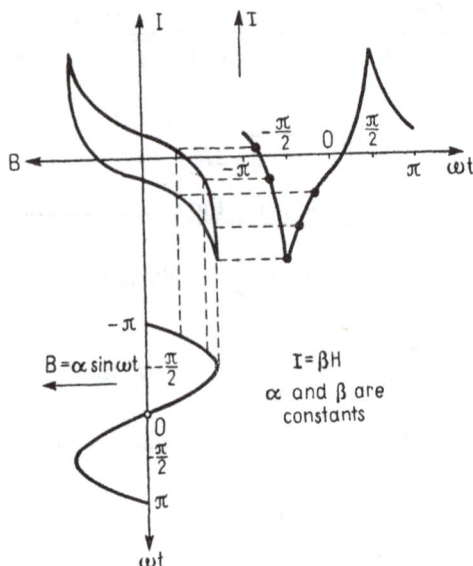

FIG. 184

action of the disc on it is expressed by the release of heat. The power $W = M_e\omega = 2\sqrt{IMH}\,\omega^2$ will be released. (3) If the needle is let free, the equation $I\dot\omega = M_e$ will hold at the initial instant. Hence

$$\dot\omega = 2\sqrt{\frac{MH}{I}}\,\omega.$$

(4) The moment produced by the earth's magnetic field will also act on the needle. If this moment is of the same order as M_e, the needle will vibrate about a new equilibrium position, given by

$$\sin\alpha = 2\sqrt{\frac{I}{MH}}\,\omega.$$

303. See Fig. 184.

304. Because the current rises much more slowly when the primary circuit is closed than it falls when the circuit is opened (see Problem 302).

305. $W = \dfrac{CU_0^2}{2} e^{-\frac{2t}{RC}}$ (Fig. 185).

306. $t \approx 7 \times 10^{-4}$ sec.

307. $W = \dfrac{E^2}{R}(1 - e^{-\frac{t}{RC}})e^{-\frac{t}{RC}}$ (Fig. 186).

308. (1) $Q = \displaystyle\int_0^\infty I^2R\,dt = \dfrac{1}{2}I_0^2R^2C = \dfrac{CE^2}{2}$; (2) $\eta = \dfrac{1}{2}$.

309. The result obtained in the answer to the previous problem, whereby the current increases instantaneously from zero to I_0, is explained by our neglecting the inductance of the circuit. Any circuit

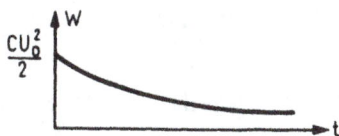

FIG. 185

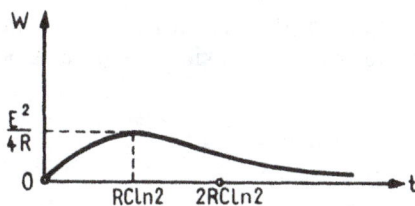

FIG. 186

contains in practice at least a small inductance, as a result of which the current rise to E/R is not instantaneous. If the inductance is small enough, the current rise is very rapid, and in many cases can be regarded as an instantaneous jump.

310. By Kirchhoff's laws, the equation for the circuit is

$$E - L\frac{dI}{dt} = RI + V \quad \text{or} \quad E = L\frac{d^2Q}{dt^2} + R\frac{dQ}{dt} + \frac{Q}{C},$$

where Q is the charge on the condenser. When $R^2 = 4L/C$, the characteristic equation has a multiple root, and the solution has to be sought in the form

$$Q = EC + (a + bt)e^{-\frac{R}{2L}t}$$

where a and b are arbitrary constants determined from the initial conditions $Q_{t=0} = 0$ and $(dQ/dt)_{t=0} = 0$. Hence

(1) $I = \dfrac{E}{L} te^{-\frac{R}{2L}t}$ (see Fig. 187); (2) $T = \dfrac{2L}{R}$; (3) $I_{\max} = \dfrac{2E}{eR}$;

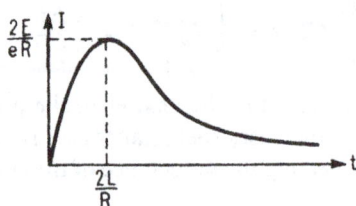

FIG. 187

(4) $V = E\dfrac{e-2}{e}$; (5) $\eta = \dfrac{1}{2}$ (e is the base of the natural logarithms).

311. We take the time when the lamp goes out as the initial instant. The voltage on the condenser at the initial instant is $V(0) = V_e$. Prior to the neon striking, the process in the circuit is given by

$$E = V + RC\frac{dV}{dt}, \tag{1}$$

where V is the voltage on the condenser at the instant t. The solution of (1) is

$$V(t) = E - (E - V_e)e^{-\frac{t}{RC}}. \tag{2}$$

At the instant $t = t_1$ the neon strikes (Fig. 188). Hence $V(t) = V_s$. We now obtain from (2):

$$t_1 = RC \ln\frac{E - V_e}{E - V_s}. \tag{3}$$

Since the lamp characteristic is linear, the current through it after striking can be written as $I_1 = (V - V_0)/R_1$, where V_0 is the voltage at which the continuation of the characteristic cuts the V axis, and $R_1 = (V_e - V_0)/I_e$ is the "equivalent resistance" of the lamp. The total current in the circuit is now

$$I = I_1 + C\frac{dV}{dt} = \frac{V - V_0}{R_1} + C\frac{dV}{dt}. \qquad (4)$$

When the lamp is burning and current passes through it, the equation of the circuit is $E = RI + V$. On substituting the value of I from (4) in this, we get

$$\frac{E}{R} + \frac{V_0}{R_1} = \left(\frac{1}{R_1} + \frac{1}{R}\right)V + C\frac{dV}{dt}. \qquad (5)$$

The general solution of this equation is

$$V(t) = \left(\frac{E}{R} + \frac{V_0}{R_1}\right)\frac{RR_1}{R + R_1} + Ae^{-\frac{(R+R_1)t}{RR_1C}}. \qquad (6)$$

We now take the time when the lamp strikes as the initial instant; then $V(0) = V_s$. We determine from this condition the constant A and substitute in (6). Finally, we substitute in the solution obtained

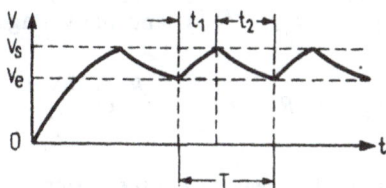

FIG. 188

$V(t_2) = V_e$ and find for the second part of the period:

$$t_2 = \frac{RR_1}{R + R_1}C\ln\frac{R(V_s - V_0) - R_1(E - V_s)}{R(V_e - V_0) - R_1(E - V_e)}.$$

The total period is

$$T = t_1 + t_2.$$

312. After closing the switch the equation of the process in the circuit is

$$E = L\frac{dI}{dt} + \frac{Rr}{R + r}I, \qquad (1)$$

where I is the total current in the circuit. At the initial instant $I_0 = E/R$, so that the solution of (1) can be written as

$$I = \frac{E(R + r)}{Rr}\left(1 - \frac{R}{R + r}e^{-\frac{Rrt}{L(R+r)}}\right).$$

The voltage between the points A and B is

$$V_{on} = I\frac{Rr}{R + r} = E\left(1 - \frac{R}{R + r}e^{-\frac{Rrt}{L(R+r)}}\right).$$

It cannot be greater than the e.m.f. of the battery. On substituting the numerical data, we get

$$V_{on} = 24(1 - 0.99e^{-2.4t}) \text{ V.}$$

After opening the switch the equation of the process in the circuit is

$$E = L\frac{dI}{dt} + RI. \tag{2}$$

At the initial instant we now have $I_0 = E(R + r)/Rr$. The solution of (2) is $I = (E/R)(1 + (R/r)e^{-Rt/L})$, and the voltage between the points A and B is

$$V_{off} = IR = E\left(1 + \frac{R}{r}e^{-\frac{Rt}{L}}\right)$$

which can be substantially greater than the battery e.m.f. if $R \gg r$. On substituting the numerical data, we get

$$V_{off} = 24(1 + 99e^{-240t}) \text{ V.}$$

At the initial instant the voltage will be 2400 V.

The present problem throws light on the processes occurring when switching on and off d.c. circuits possessing resistance and inductance.

313. After switching off, the equation of the process in the circuit is

$$E = L\frac{dI}{dt} + V. \tag{1}$$

But $I = C\,dV/dt$. The initial conditions are $V_0 = E$, $I_0 = E/r$. Hence the solution of equation (1) is

$$V = E\left(1 + \frac{1}{r}\sqrt{\frac{L}{C}}\,\sin\frac{2\pi}{\sqrt{LC}}\,t\right).$$

On substituting the numerical data, we obtain for the maximum value of the voltage $V_{max} = (\sqrt{10}\times 100 + 24)$ V. An increase in the capacity C leads to a reduction in V_{max}.

§ 6. ALTERNATING CURRENTS

314. The important figure when charging an accumulator is the average of the current I_{av}, whereas an electrodynamic ammeter indicates the effective value I_{eff}. Since $I_{av} = (2\sqrt{2}/\pi)\,I_{eff} \approx 0.9\,I_{eff}$, the charging time will be $8/0.9 = 8.8$ hr.

315. $I_{av} \approx 0.127$ amp.

316. (1) ≈ 3.2 amp, (2) 5 amp.

317. (1) 314 V, (2) 157 V.

318. The valves pass current alternately every $\frac{1}{2}$ period. The condensers are then charged so that the potential differences across them add up. If the load resistance is high, almost all the current during a half-period goes into charging the condenser. Hence $V_{max} \approx 2V_0$, where V_0 is the amplitude of the voltage over CD.

319. 14.2 amp.

320. $\mu \approx 2900$.

321. The current has a phase lead over the voltage of $\varphi = 88°$.

322. $R = 54.4$ ohm; $C \approx 100\ \mu F$.

323. $\tan\varphi = \omega CR$.

324. $\alpha = \arctan\dfrac{L\omega}{R}$.

325. When the plane of the frame is at right angles to the field.

326. When the plane of the frame forms an angle

$$\varphi = \arctan \frac{\omega L - \dfrac{1}{\omega C}}{R}$$

with the direction of the field.

327. $R = \sqrt{\dfrac{L}{C(1 - \omega^2 LC)}}$.

328. $I_{max} \approx 1 \cdot 2$ amp; $\varphi \approx 43°$; $W \approx 76$ W.

329. $W = \dfrac{V^2 - V_1^2 - V_2^2}{2R}$.

330. $W = \dfrac{(I^2 - I_1^2 - I_2^2)R}{2}$.

331. $W \approx 40 \mu$W.

332. (1) $I_1 = \dfrac{3E}{N(9r + 2R)}$, (2) $I_2 = \dfrac{6E}{N(9r + 2R)}$;

the currents are in opposite directions.

333. In this case the inductance L of the turn cannot be neglected, and the current is given by $-L dI/dt = E$. Depending on the size and specific resistance of the material of the turn and the e.m.f. supply frequency, either only the ohmic or only the inductive impedance, or both, of the turn need be taken into account.

334. $r = \dfrac{R}{\sqrt{1 + R^2 C^2 \omega^2}}$.

335. $L = CR^2$.

336. The phase displacement between the points is $\varphi = \arctan(1/\omega R_1 C)$, i.e. it is independent of R_2. When the resistance R_1 changes from zero to ∞, the phase displacement changes from $\frac{1}{2}\pi$ to zero, whilst the current through R_2 lags in phase behind the current through R_1.

337. $E = I_0 \dfrac{\sqrt{1 + R^2 C^2 \omega^2}}{C\omega} \sin(\omega t + \varphi),$

$I_1 = \dfrac{I_0 \sqrt{1 + R^2 C^2 \omega^2}}{\omega^2 LC} \cos(\omega t + \varphi); \quad \tan \varphi = R\omega C.$

338. $r = \dfrac{\sqrt{R^2 + \omega^2 L^2}}{\sqrt{(1 - \omega^2 LC)^2 + \omega^2 R^2 C^2}};$

the maximum value is $r_{max} \approx L/RC$, attained when $\omega = 1/\sqrt{LC}$.

339. Because, whatever the charge on the condenser plates, the potential difference between them is zero. In accordance with this, in the case of an a.c. circuit, when a condenser is short-circuited, its capacitative impedance is $X_C = 1/\omega C = 0$, i.e. $C = \infty$.

340. $U_2 \approx [10 \sin(300t - 132°) + 3 \sin(600t + 207°)]$ V.

341. $E \approx 150 \cos(600t - 78°)$ V.

342. The equations for the transformer circuits can be written in the complex form as

$$\left. \begin{aligned} E &= j\omega L_1 I_1 + j\omega M I_2, \\ 0 &= j\omega M I_1 + j\omega L_2 I_2 + R I_2. \end{aligned} \right\} \tag{1}$$

For a transformer without leakage, the mutual inductance $M = \sqrt{L_1 L_2}$ and $L_2/L_1 = n^2$. Hence we obtain from equations (1):

$$E = \frac{j\omega L_1 R}{j\omega L_1 n^2 + R} \times I_1 = Z I_1.$$

The complex impedance of the equivalent circuit (see Fig.101 (b)) is

$$Z = \frac{j\omega L_1 R/n^2}{j\omega L_1 + R/n^2}.$$

343. (1) Zero; (2) the current through the resistance lags in phase by 90°; (3) the phase shift is

$$\varphi = \arctan \frac{\omega(L + CrR)}{r + R(1 - \omega^2 CL)}$$

the voltage is in advance of the e.m.f.

344. $E_{\text{eff}}^2 = \dfrac{4}{T}\displaystyle\int_0^{T/4}\left(\dfrac{4E_0}{T}t\right)^2 dt = \dfrac{E_0^2}{3}$.

345. See Fig. 189.

346. $\omega \approx 3{\cdot}16 \times 10^6 \ \text{sec}^{-1}$; $\theta = 0{\cdot}25$; $I_0 \approx 1{\cdot}6 \ \text{amp}$.

347. $C \approx 50 \ \mu\text{F}$; $V_{\text{max}} \approx 628 \ \text{V}$.

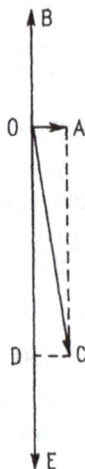

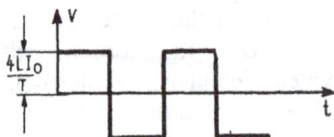

FIG. 189   FIG. 190

348. $C \approx 20 \ \mu\text{F}$. We shall solve the problem in the vector form. In Fig. 190, OA is the voltage drop in the ohmic resistance (10 V); OB is the voltage drop in the coil (62·8 V); OC is the total voltage (100 V); $OD \approx OC$; OE is the voltage drop in the condenser (163 V). Hence $C = I/\omega V \approx 20 \ \mu\text{F}$.

349. $C \approx 0{\cdot}32 \ \mu\text{F}$.

350. Kirchhoff's equations for the two circuits can be written in the complex form as

$$E = I\left[R + j\omega\left(L - \dfrac{1}{\omega^2 C}\right)\right] + I'j\omega\left(M - \dfrac{1}{\omega^2 C}\right),$$

$$0 = I\left(M - \dfrac{1}{\omega^2 C}\right) + I'\left(L' - \dfrac{1}{\omega^2 C}\right),$$

where I and I' are the currents in branches A and B respectively. It follows from the last equation that (1) if $\omega = 1/\sqrt{MC}$, then $I' = 0$; (2) if $\omega = 1/\sqrt{LC}$, then $I = 0$.

Note. This case has only become possible because we have neglected the resistance in the circuit B.

351. (1) $I_0 \approx 0 \cdot 8$ amp; $W \approx 32$ W, (2) $I_0' = 2$ amp.

352. (1) $W = \dfrac{E_0^2 R}{R^2 + \left(\omega L - \dfrac{1}{\omega C}\right)^2}$; (2) $C = \dfrac{1}{\omega^2 L}$;

(3) $W_{max} = \dfrac{E_0^2}{R}$.

353. $W = \dfrac{E^2 (R + R_0)}{\omega^2 (L + L_0)^2 + (R + R_0)^2}$;

$W' = \dfrac{E^2 R}{\omega^2 (L + L_0)^2 + (R + R_0)^2}$; $\eta = \dfrac{R}{R + R_0}$.

Note. As may be seen, η is independent of the inductance of the line, though the power which the source can supply for a given voltage E decreases as L and L_0 increase.

354. $W = \dfrac{E_0^2 [R + (1 + \alpha^2) r]}{2[(r + R)^2 + \alpha^2 r^2]}$; $\eta = \dfrac{R}{R + (1 + \alpha^2) r}$;

where $\alpha = \omega RC$.

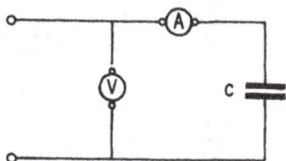

FIG. 191

Note. As distinct from the previous problem, here both the power W that can be delivered by the source and the efficiency η of the arrangement are reduced when α increases.

355. The amplitude of the source e.m.f. is $E_0 = \sqrt{3} \times 120$ V; $\eta = \frac{1}{3}$; $\eta' = \frac{1}{2}$.

356. The amplitude of the source of e.m.f. is $E_0 \approx 140$ V.

357. The circuit is shown in Fig. 191. $C = I/\omega V$ F, where I is in amperes, V in volts, and ω is the angular frequency of the supply current.

358. $C \approx 6 \cdot 3 \ \mu\text{F}$.

359. The leakage resistance of the condenser must be much greater than its capacitative impedance to 50 c/s current.

360. First find the leakage resistance by means of a d.c. measurement, then the total impedance to a.c.:

$$\frac{R}{\sqrt{1 + \omega^2 R^2 C^2}}.$$

361. $C_x/C_1 = AD/DB$. It is possible.

362. It is possible if $\omega^2 = 1/C_1 L_1 = 1/C_2 L_2$. In fact, if the instrument G remains at zero, the voltage at the point A is

$$\frac{V \dfrac{1}{j\omega C_1}}{\dfrac{1}{j\omega C_1} + j\omega L_2} = \frac{V}{1 - \omega^2 C_1 L_2},$$

and at the point B:

$$\frac{V j\omega L_1}{j\omega L_1 + \dfrac{1}{j\omega C_2}} = \frac{V}{1 - \dfrac{1}{\omega^2 L_1 C_2}}$$

so that

$$\omega^2 C_1 L_2 = \frac{1}{\omega^2 L_1 C_2}$$

or

$$\omega^4 C_1 C_2 L_1 L_2 = 1.$$

The answer follows from this.

363. (1) $\tan \varphi = \dfrac{2RC\omega}{1 - R^2 C^2 \omega^2}$,   (2) $\varphi = \pm \dfrac{\pi}{2}$.

364. $C \approx 15 \ \mu\text{F}$.

365. $L = 2 \cdot 3 \ \text{H}$; the first condenser does not affect the ratio of the output to input amplitudes.

366. The transformer only consumes a significant power when the button is pressed. When the button is not pressed, a small "idling" current

$$I_{\text{idling}} = \frac{E}{\sqrt{R^2 + \omega^2 L^2}}$$

flows in the primary, where E is the input voltage, R the primary winding resistance, L is inductance and ω the circular frequency of the current. When $\omega L \gg R$ the transformer consumes almost no power from the idling current ("wattless current"). The button is not connected in the secondary circuit because this would mean subjecting it to high voltage.

367. 7 H.

368. The primary is 200 turns, the secondary 6600 turns.

Hint. The e.m.f. induced in one turn is the same in all the windings of the transformer.

369. (1) $L \approx 0{\cdot}3$ H,   (2) $V \approx 3760$ V.

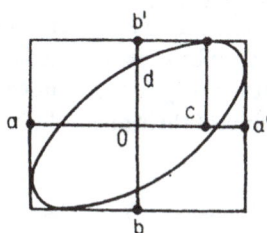

FIG. 192

370. $I \approx \dfrac{ES\omega\alpha}{4\pi d_0} \sin \omega t.$

371. $C = 320$ pF.

372. $C = 0{\cdot}1\ \mu\text{F}.$

373. (1) $R \approx 6370$ ohm,   (2) $R \approx 3185$ ohm or $R \approx 12{,}740$ ohm.

374. $\frac{4}{5}$ radius.

375. (1) Coordinate axes are first marked off on the tube screen (Fig. 192): the current I_1 only is switched on and the magnitude and position of the axis $a - a'$ marked, then I_2 only is switched on and the magnitude and position of the axis $b - b'$ marked. The rectangle is marked out. When both currents are switched on, the spot describes an ellipse. (All this can be photographed.) Now

$$\frac{Oc}{Oa'} = \cos\varphi \quad \text{and} \quad \frac{Od}{Ob'} = \sin\varphi,$$

where φ (or $180° - \varphi$) is the phase difference.

(2) It cannot.

376. $\cos\varphi = \dfrac{1}{2}\tan 2\alpha \left(\dfrac{a}{b} - \dfrac{b}{a}\right),$

where α is the angle of the slope of the major axis of the ellipse, a and b are the major and minor semi-axes of the ellipse.

377. The necessary data are: (1) the sensitivity of the cathode ray oscilloscope (the beam deviation as a function of the voltage); (2) the size of the resistance R. On closing K_1, the input voltage is measured. After closing K_2 only, the voltage drop in the known resistance R is measured and the current obtained. Then, after closing both switches, an ellipse is obtained, from the parameters of which the phase shift is easily found. Knowing the input voltage, the current in the circuit and their phase difference, the power may be found.

378. $R_1 = \dfrac{r_{12}r_{13}}{r_{12} + r_{13} + r_{23}}; \quad R_2 = \dfrac{r_{12}r_{23}}{r_{12} + r_{13} + r_{23}};$

$R_3 = \dfrac{r_{13}r_{23}}{r_{12} + r_{13} + r_{23}}.$

379. A load $p \approx 17$ g has to be added.

380. $120°$ or $240°$.

381. (1) They are unaffected; (2) twisting occurs in the opposite direction; (3) it cannot.

382. $I = (6 - 5e^{-50t})$ amp.

383. $I = (1 + 10e^{-2\times 10^{-5}t})$ amp   (Fig. 193).

384. $I = \dfrac{0 \cdot 05}{7} \sin \omega t$ amp; $\omega = \dfrac{2}{7} \times 10^4$ sec^{-1}.

385. $V = 5(1 - e^{-4 \times 10^4 t})$ V.

386. $V \approx 6 \cdot 3 e^{-250t} \sin 660t$ V.

387. $q = \dfrac{EC}{2} \left[1 - \left(\cos \omega_1 t + \dfrac{\delta}{\omega_1} \sin \omega_1 t \right) e^{-\delta t} \right]$, where

$$\omega_1 = \sqrt{\dfrac{1}{LC} - \dfrac{r^2}{16L^2}}, \quad \delta = \dfrac{r}{4L}.$$

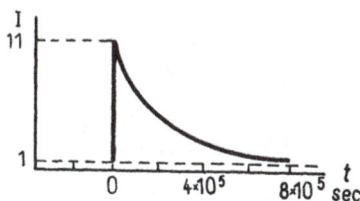

Fig. 193

388. $I = \left[\dfrac{1}{5} - \dfrac{\sqrt{2}}{5} e^{-2000t} \sin(2000t + 45°) \right]$ amp.

389. $V \approx 20 \left(\cos 20\pi t - \cos \dfrac{100}{35} t \right)$ mV.

390. $I = \dfrac{1}{\pi} (1 - \cos 100 \pi t)$ amp. As we see, the current in the circuit is pulsating and not alternating. This result is explained by the fact we have neglected the ohmic resistance of the circuit and have specially chosen the initial phase of switching on the e.m.f. The d.c. component of the current produced at the initial instant is not damped, but circulates all the time and is added to the alternating component. In an actual circuit possessing resistance, the d.c. component will be absent and the steady-state current is alternating. To appreciate the role of the resistance, it is useful to analyse the case when the given e.m.f. is switched on to a coil with resistance R, then pass to the limit $R = 0$ in the answer (see Problem 392).

391. $I = 0.5 \cos 200\pi t$ amp.

$$V \approx 104(\cos \sqrt{10} \times 1000t - \cos 200\pi t) \text{ V.}$$

The natural oscillations of the voltage across the condenser are thus undamped, although the resistance R is present, and they have no influence on the magnitude of the current through R, since the internal resistance of the source is assumed zero. Thus the source "short circuits" the resistance, the voltage across which is always equal to the source e.m.f. In an actual circuit, in which the source always possesses internal resistance, the natural oscillations are damped and only the forced oscillations remain.

392. $V = \dfrac{100}{\sqrt{2}} \cos\left(100\pi t - \dfrac{\pi}{4}\right) - 50e^{-314t}$ V.

393. $I = -\dfrac{1}{4\sqrt{2}} \sin\left(250\pi t - \dfrac{\pi}{4}\right) + \dfrac{1}{8} e^{-250t}$ amp.

394. $Q_1 = \dfrac{CV_0}{2}(1 + \cos\omega t)$ on the condenser which was charged. $Q_2 = \dfrac{CV_0}{2}(1 - \cos\omega t)$ on the second; $\omega = \sqrt{2/LC}$.

395. $L \approx 1$ H.

396. $T \approx 58 \times 10^{-6}$ sec.

397. $\lambda \approx 126$ km.

398. $C \approx 110$ pF.

399. $I_0 = \dfrac{V_0}{\sqrt{L/C}}$; the quantity $\sqrt{L/C}$ is called the "characteristic" or "wave" impedance of the circuit.

400. $f \approx 5000$ sec^{-1}.

401. $\dfrac{\Delta\omega}{\omega_0} \approx \dfrac{1}{\pi}$ per cent.

402. $\dfrac{1}{R} = \dfrac{1}{R_1} + \dfrac{1}{R_2},$

$\dfrac{1}{L} = \dfrac{1}{L_1} + \dfrac{1}{L_2}$ $\Bigg\}$ parallel connection

and

$R = R_1 + R_2,$

$L = L_1 + L_2$ $\Bigg\}$ series connection

403. The condenser is fitted to prevent the possibility of a substantial current from the mains travelling through the receiver input circuit to earth. Its capacity should be roughly equal to the normal capacity of an aerial (200–300 cm), to prevent its having any substantial effect on the wavelength range to which the input circuit can be tuned.

404. $R \approx 40$ ohm.

405. Approximately 12 periods.

406. The damping factor characterises the time taken for the amplitude of the circuit oscillations to be reduced e times. The logarithmic decrement characterises the number of periods required for the amplitude of the oscillations to be reduced e times.

407. $\dfrac{4L}{R}$ sec $= 2 \times 10^{-5}$ sec.

408. 2400 μH; 400 μH.

409. Join the coils in series and measure their total inductance L_1, then interchange the ends of one coil and again measure the inductance L_2. Then

$$M = \frac{L_1 - L_2}{4}.$$

410. At low frequencies the voltage across the inductance is close to zero, and almost equal to the e.m.f. across the capacity; at high frequencies, vice versa.

411. $I = \dfrac{ERC\omega}{\sqrt{L^2\omega^2 + R^2}}$; $\tan \varphi = \dfrac{-R}{L\omega}.$

412. The current remains unchanged. The resonant frequency increases $\sqrt{2}$ times.

413. At resonance the power dissipated by the source of e.m.f. is $W = E^2R/(L^2\omega^2 + R^2)$. If $L\omega \gg R$, the power falls to a quarter when L is doubled.

414. *Hint.* Transform the usual formula

$$I = \frac{E}{\sqrt{R^2 + \left(L\omega - \dfrac{1}{\omega C}\right)^2}}$$

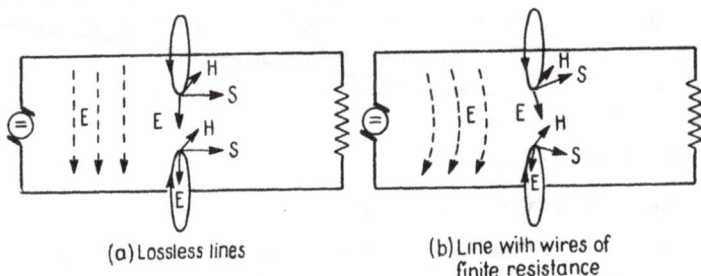

(a) Lossless lines

(b) Line with wires of finite resistance

Fig. 194

for the current in the circuit by substituting in it $I_0 = E/R$; $\omega_0 = 2\pi f_0 = 1/\sqrt{LC}$ and the frequency of the external e.m.f. is $\omega = 2\pi(f_0 + \Delta f)$. Neglect squares and higher powers.

415. The decrement and damping factor are doubled, the current in the circuit is unchanged, and the voltage across the condenser is halved.

416. $Q = \dfrac{1}{2\pi f_{res}RC} \approx 50$.

417. $Q = 30$.

418. The Q of the circuit must be $Q > 100$, i.e. the logarithmic decrement of the circuit less than 3 per cent.

419. $\approx 0{\cdot}2$ per cent.

420. See Fig. 194. When resistance is present in the conductors there is a voltage drop along them, i.e. there exists on their surfaces

and in the space between them a tangential component of the vector
E, as a result of which the Poynting vector is bent towards the
conductors. Part of the energy flows into the load and part into the
conductors where it is transformed into heat.

421. Since E and H change their direction simultaneously, the
vector S does not change direction.

422. Since the instants when the vectors E and H reverse their
directions are a quarter period apart, the vector S will reverse its
direction every quarter period.

For, in this case

$$\int_0^T \frac{EH}{4\pi}\, dt = \int_0^T \frac{1}{4\pi} E_0 \sin \omega t\, H_0 \cos \omega t\, dt = 0.$$

The energy oscillates in individual sections of the line, but does
not flow in one direction (standing waves).

423. (1) See Fig. 195;

$$(2)\; S \times 2\pi r l = \frac{1}{4\pi} EH \times 2\pi r l = \frac{1}{4\pi} \times \frac{V}{l} \times \frac{2I}{r} 2\pi r l = VI.$$

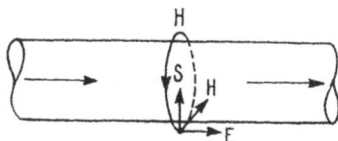

FIG. 195

424. (1) $j_c = \dfrac{1}{4\pi} \dfrac{\partial D}{\partial t} = 0;$ (2) $j_c = \dfrac{1}{4\pi} \dfrac{\partial D}{\partial t} = -\dfrac{1}{4\pi} \dfrac{VU}{d^2};$

(3) the displacement current changes sign.

§ 7. ELECTRIC CURRENTS IN LIQUIDS

425. It moves counter-clockwise (viewed from above).

426. The amount of material deposited corresponds to 1 Coulomb
at the anode and 1 Coulomb at the cathode, since not only do positive ions with $\frac{1}{2}$ Coulomb charge arrive at the cathode in 1 sec, but

negative ions with $\frac{1}{2}$ Coulomb charge at the same time leave the
cathode, thereby releasing at the cathode the same number of
positive ions, whose charge is $\frac{1}{2}$ Coulomb.

427. $\approx 26\cdot8$ ampere-hours.

428. $\dfrac{e}{m_\mathrm{H}} \approx 2\cdot9 \times 10^{14}$ e.s.u.

429. $m_\mathrm{H} = 1\cdot65 \times 10^{-24}$ g; $\quad e = 4\cdot77 \times 10^{-10}$ e.s.u.

430. $Q \approx 4$ mg.

431. $I = 4\cdot5$ amp.

432. The following essential fact is overlooked in the arguments.
When a substance is liberated at the electrodes of an electrolytic
bath polarisation of the electrodes occurs, as a result of which a
reverse e.m.f. is obtained. (This is analogous to the appearance of
an e.m.f. in accumulators when they are on charge.) When several
baths containing acidified water are joined in series, the back
e.m.f.'s of the baths add up and in the long run will reach the value
of the e.m.f. of the battery before the amount of electricity which it is
capable of supplying has been taken from it, and the current ceases.

433. $E \approx 1\cdot06$ V.

434. $Nu/(u + v)$ Coulombs for the anions, $Nv/(u + v)$ Coulombs
for the cations.

435. About $2\cdot5$ times greater.

436. $0\cdot844$ and $0\cdot156$.

437. $k \approx 0\cdot473$.

438. $k \approx 0\cdot497$.

439. By interaction of the cation with the electrolyte, as a result
of which a compound is formed, containing the cation material
and representing the anion in solution. In the present case of
electrolysis of CdI_2 the ions are $\frac{1}{2}$ Cd and $\frac{1}{2}$ $(CdI_2 + I_2)$.

440. $A = N\dfrac{vRT}{(u + v)nF} \ln \dfrac{C_1}{C_2}$, where F is Faraday's number,
n is the valency.

441. The method of solution follows from the previous problem.

442. $k = \dfrac{RT}{nF} u$, where F is Faraday's number, R is the gas constant, n the number of gram-equivalents of ion per unit volume or the valency of the ion.

443. The processes occurring during the charge and discharge of a lead accumulator can be represented by the following chemical formula:

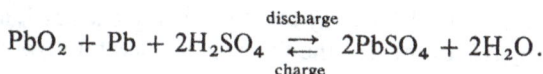

$$PbO_2 + Pb + 2H_2SO_4 \overset{\text{discharge}}{\underset{\text{charge}}{\rightleftarrows}} 2PbSO_4 + 2H_2O.$$

Hence it follows that the density of the electrolyte increases at the expense of the H_2SO_4.

§ 8. THERMOELECTRICITY

444. 8×10^{-5} amp.

445. $C = 5 \times 10^{-5}$ V deg^{-1}.

446. $T_1 = 1015°C$.

447. (1) $V = \dfrac{A_2 - A_1}{e} + \dfrac{kT}{e} \ln \dfrac{p_1}{p_2}$,

(2) $V_1 - V_2 = \dfrac{k(T_1 - T_2)}{e} \ln \dfrac{p_1}{p_2}$.

§ 9. ELECTRONICS

448. $v \approx 59 \cdot 5 \times 10^7$ cm sec^{-1}.

449. $v \approx 0 \cdot 7 \times 10^{-4}$ cm sec^{-1}.

450. $V = IB/can$, where c is the velocity of light.

451. $V = 300 \left[\dfrac{2RI_h \Delta I_h}{I} - \dfrac{2kT}{e} \right]$.

Solution. If T is the temperature to which the filament is heated, by comparison with which the temperature of the conductor along which the electrons return to the filament can be neglected, the average kinetic energy of the emitted electron is $2kT$ by Richardson's law, where k is Boltzmann's constant. In addition, the filament loses energy expended in removing the electron, i.e. $1/300 \times Ve$, where V is the work function expressed in volts, and e is the charge on the electron. If I is the emission current, I/e electrons are removed per second, so that the filament loses energy

$$I(V/300 + 2kT/e)$$

per second. Due to this energy loss the heating current I_h has to be increased by ΔI_h to prevent the filament temperature from falling. The increase of ΔI_h in the heating current releases extra energy $2RI_h\,\Delta I_h$, where R is the resistance of the hot filament. This extra energy compensates all the energy loss of the filament, so that we have

$$I\left(\frac{V}{300} + \frac{2kT}{e}\right) = 2RI_h\Delta I_h.$$

Hence follows the answer.

452. The speed is from 56 to 60 V, due to the fact that there is a drop of 4 V along the heater, i.e. it is not at the same potential throughout. This velocity distribution holds when the anode current is small compared with the heater current, as is usually the case.

453. The final velocity of the electrons at the anode remains the same, since the electrons travel through the same potential difference in both cases. However, the electron velocities at intermediate points between the cathode and anode are different in the two cases, since the new grid connection causes a change in the potential distribution in the electric field inside the valve.

454. $E = \dfrac{2dV}{l\left(D + \dfrac{l}{2}\right)}.$

455. $T = \dfrac{2\pi m}{He}$, i.e. depends neither on v_0 nor on α.

456. $r = \dfrac{mv}{He}.$

457. Zero, since the force acting on the electron is always at right angles to its displacement.

458. $AB = \dfrac{2\pi m v \cos \alpha}{He}$.

459. $I = \dfrac{D}{\pi n(D^2 - d^2)} \sqrt{\dfrac{2Vm}{e}}$.

460. (1) If we take the origin at the point of departure of the electron and the x axis at right angles to the plates in the opposite direction to the electric field, and the y axis parallel to the plates and perpendicular to the magnetic field, the electron path is given by the equations

$$x = \frac{Emc^2}{H^2 e}\left(1 - \cos\frac{He}{mc}t\right); \quad y = \frac{Emc^2}{H^2 e}\left(\frac{He}{mc}t - \sin\frac{He}{mc}t\right).$$

(2) $\dfrac{2Emc^2}{H^2 e} < d; \quad y = \dfrac{\pi mc^2 E}{H^2 c}$,

where d is the distance between the plates, e is the charge on the electron, m is the mass of the electron, c is the velocity of light.

461. The components of the initial velocity along (V_{y_0}) and perpendicular to (V_{x_0}) the cathode plate must be

$$V_{y_0} = -\frac{E}{H}; \quad V_{x_0} = 0; \quad R = \frac{Em}{H^2 e}; \quad T = \frac{2\pi m}{He}.$$

462. $M = \dfrac{mv^2}{2H}$.

463. $\mathfrak{M} = \dfrac{m^2 v^2}{eH}$.

464. $R \approx 1{\cdot}9 \times 10^{-13}$ cm.

465. $x = R\left(1 - \cos\dfrac{eH}{mc}t\right)$, $y = \dfrac{cE}{H}t + R\sin\dfrac{eH}{mc}t$, where

$R = \dfrac{mc}{eH}\left(v - \dfrac{cE}{H}\right)$;

the x axis is parallel to the electric field, the y axis at right angles to both fields.

466. $v = \dfrac{c[E \wedge H]}{H^2}$.

467. $\dfrac{e}{m} = \dfrac{\omega^2 l^2}{2\pi^2 V(2n-1)^2}$, where n is an integer.

468. $\varrho = Ea^3$.

469. $\omega = \dfrac{e}{m} B \approx 25 \times 10^{10}$ sec^{-1}.

470. $r_N : r_1 = \sqrt{N}$, where N is the number of semicircles described by a deuteron after release.

471. $q = \dfrac{I_{sat}}{eSd} \approx 0.6 \times 10^{10}$.

472. There is a space charge between the condenser plates, the density of which at a distance x from the cathode is equal to $\varrho(x)$. Hence

$$\frac{d^2 V}{dx^2} = -4\pi\varrho(x). \tag{1}$$

If the electron mobility is u, the current density is

$$j = -\varrho(x)uE = -\varrho(x)\,u\,\frac{dV}{dx}. \tag{2}$$

We obtain from (1) and (2):

$$\frac{dV}{dx}\frac{d^2V}{dx^2} = \frac{4\pi j}{u} \quad \text{or} \quad \frac{d}{dx}\left(\frac{dV}{dx}\right)^2 = \frac{8\pi j}{u}. \tag{3}$$

When the current reaches saturation, we have $(dV/dx)_{x=0} = 0$ for $x = 0$ and $j = j_{sat}$. Hence we obtain, on integrating (3):

$$\frac{dV}{dx} = \sqrt{\frac{8\pi j_{sat}}{u}}\, x^{1/2},$$

Further integration yields

$$V_0 = \frac{2}{3} \sqrt{\frac{8\pi j_{sat}}{u}} \, d^{3/2},$$

whence

$$u = \frac{32\pi}{9} \frac{d^3 I_{sat}}{SV_0^2}.$$

473. $u = \dfrac{ldI}{2c\theta}$.

474. $I = n_0 e \varepsilon^{\alpha d}$, where ε is the base of natural logarithms, and e is the charge on an electron.

475. $I = \dfrac{n_0 e (\varepsilon^{\alpha d} - 1)}{\alpha}$, where ε is the base of natural logarithms and e is the charge on an electron.

476. $v = \sqrt{\dfrac{2e\varphi}{m}} = 1920$ km sec^{-1}.

477. The positive column is shortened.

478. In addition to the longitudinal potential gradient, there is a transverse gradient due to charge diffusion to the walls of the tube.

479. Because the electric field at the cathode surface is perpendicular to this surface and is much stronger than in the remaining space in the tube (cathode drop).

480. *Solution.* If the ion mass is m, its distance from the common centre of mass is r, and the frequency of rotation ω, the total kinetic energy of the ion rotation is

$$\frac{m_1 r_1^2 \omega^2}{2} + \frac{m_2 (d - r_1)^2 \omega^2}{2},$$

where d is the distance between the ions. In accordance with the law of uniform distribution of energy with respect to the degrees of freedom, this energy is equal to kT. On the other hand, a centrifugal force acts on each ion, equal to the force of interaction between the ions. Consequently,

$$m_1 \omega^2 r_1 = m_2 \omega^2 (d - r_1) = \frac{e^2}{d^2}.$$

We find from these equations:

$$2kT = \frac{e^2 r_1}{d^2} + \frac{e^2(d - r_1)}{d^2} = \frac{e^2}{d}.$$

Hence $d = e^2/2kT$, so that the required electric moment is

$$\mu = de = \frac{e^3}{2kT} \approx 1\cdot4 \times 10^{-16} \text{ e.s.u.}$$

§ 10. ELECTROMAGNETIC WAVES

481. $U_x = U_0 \cos \dfrac{k\pi x}{l}$; $I_x = I_0 \sin \dfrac{k\pi x}{l}$,

where U_0 is the voltage amplitude at the voltage loop, I_0 the current amplitude at the current loop, x the distance from the start of the

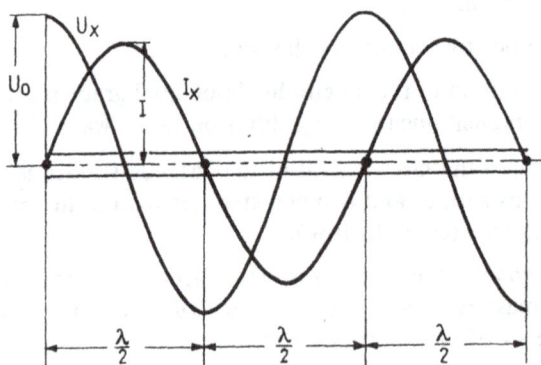

FIG. 196

lines, k the number of the harmonic ($k = 1, 2, 3, \ldots$). $\nu_k = kc/2l$, where c is the velocity of the wave propagation along the line (for a line in air $c = 300,000$ km/sec).

Figure 196 shows the amplitude distributions for one of the natural oscillations (third harmonic).

482. $U_x = U_0 \sin \dfrac{k\pi x}{l}$, $I_x = I_0 \cos \dfrac{k\pi x}{l}$, $\nu_k = \dfrac{kc}{2l}$.

The notation is the same as in the previous answer. The amplitude distributions for one of the natural oscillations (fourth harmonic) are shown in Fig. 197.

483. $U_x = U_0 \cos \dfrac{2k + 1}{2} \dfrac{\pi x}{l}$; $\quad I_x = I_0 \sin \dfrac{2k + 1}{2} \dfrac{\pi x}{l}$,

$$v_k = \frac{2k + 1}{4} \frac{c}{l},$$

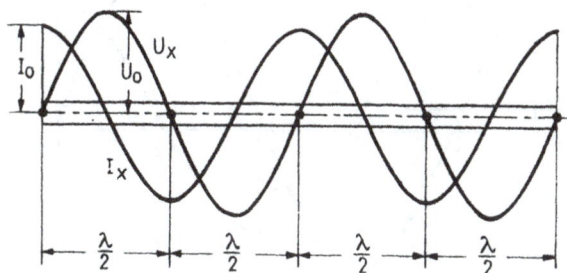

FIG. 197

x is the distance from the open circuit end of the line, $k = 0, 1, 2, 3, \ldots$, ($2k + 1$ is the number of the harmonic). The amplitude distributions for one of the natural oscillations (fifth harmonic) are shown in Fig. 198.

484. $\varrho = 120 \ln \dfrac{d}{r} \approx 468$ ohm.

Solution. We consider an element of line of length dx (Fig. 199) and write down the two Kirchhoff equations for the element:

$$i(x + dx) - i(x) = C_1 dx \frac{\partial u}{\partial t}, \quad \text{or} \quad \frac{\partial i}{\partial x} = C_1 \frac{\partial u}{\partial t}, \qquad (1)$$

$$u(x + dx) - u(x) = L_1 dx \frac{\partial i}{\partial t}, \quad \text{or} \quad \frac{\partial u}{\partial x} = L_1 \frac{\partial i}{\partial t}, \qquad (2)$$

where C_1 and L_1 are the capacity and inductance per unit length of the line. On differentiating one equation with respect to x and the other with respect to t, and eliminating one of the unknowns, we obtain the equations for the current and voltage:

$$\frac{\partial^2 i}{\partial x^2} = L_1 C_1 \frac{\partial^2 i}{\partial i^2}, \tag{3}$$

$$\frac{\partial^2 u}{\partial x^2} = L_1 C_1 \frac{\partial^2 u}{\partial t^2}. \tag{4}$$

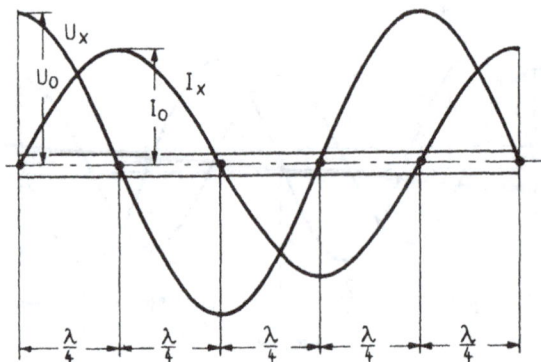

FIG. 198

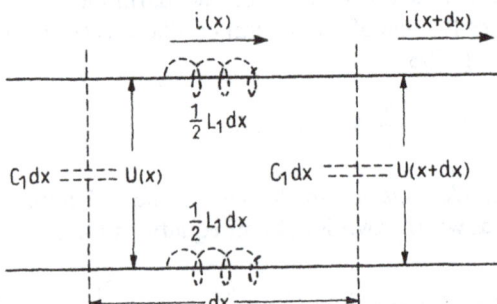

FIG. 199

If the voltage and current at every point of the line vary harmonically in time (angular frequency ω), the solutions of (3) and (4) are of the form

$$i = I_0 \sin \omega \left(t - \frac{x}{v} \right); \quad u = U_0 \sin \omega \left(t - \frac{x}{v} \right),$$

where $v = 1/\sqrt{L_1 C_1}$ is the velocity of wave propagation along the line. On substituting these solutions in (1), we obtain the ratio of the voltage to current amplitudes, i.e. the characteristic impedance of the line:

$$\varrho = \left| \frac{U_0}{I_0} \right| = \frac{1}{v C_1} = \sqrt{\frac{L_1}{C_1}},$$

where ϱ is in ohms if L_1 and C_1 are in practical units. Since we always have $v \approx 3 \times 10^{10}$ cm/sec for an air-spaced line, the formula $\varrho = 1/v C_1$ is generally used, the line capacity being measured per cm of line if the velocity is expressed in cm/sec. If the capacity is in e.s.u. (i.e. in centimetres), then

$$\varrho = \frac{30}{C_1(\text{cm}/\text{cm})} \text{ ohm}.$$

On substituting the value of the capacity between two parallel wires, per cm of their length,

$$C_1 = \frac{1}{4 \ln (d/r)}.$$

we obtain the expression given in the answer.

485. $\varrho = 60 \ln \dfrac{R}{r} \approx 97$ ohm.

Solution. Since the coaxial line is air-spaced, the same expression as in the previous problem holds for the characteristic impedance. On substituting in this expression the capacity per cm of concentric line,

$$C_1 = \frac{1}{2 \ln (R/r)},$$

we obtain the expression given in the answer.

486. $v = \dfrac{c}{\sqrt{\varepsilon}} \approx 1 \cdot 43 \times 10^{10}$ cm sec^{-1}.

487. $T_k = \dfrac{2l}{kv}$, where k is the number of the harmonic and

$v = c/\sqrt{\varepsilon} = 3\cdot3 \times 10^9$ cm/sec is the velocity of electromagnetic wave propagation in water (the dielectric constant of water $\varepsilon \approx 80$).

488. $\nu_1 = \dfrac{v}{4l} \approx 3000$ c/s.

489. $\varrho = \dfrac{60 \ln (R/r)}{\sqrt{\varepsilon}} \approx 68$ ohm.

Solution. The characteristic impedance $\varrho = 1/vC_1$, and since v is $\sqrt{\varepsilon}$ times smaller than *in vacuo*, whilst C_1 is ε times greater, the characteristic impedance is $\sqrt{\varepsilon}$ times less than for the same cable with air spacing (see the solutions to Problems 484, 485).

490. $Z_{\text{in}} = \left| \varrho \cot \dfrac{2\pi l}{\lambda} \right|$. Hence, if the wavelength $\lambda = c/v = 6$ m, we have

(1) $Z_{\text{in}} = |216 \cot \tfrac{2}{3}\pi| \approx 130$ ohm (inductive)

(2) $Z_{\text{in}} = |216 \cot \pi| = \infty$ (parallel resonance)

(3) $Z_{\text{in}} = |216 \cot \tfrac{7}{6}\pi| \approx 374$ ohm (capacitative)

(4) $Z_{\text{in}} = |216 \cot \tfrac{5}{2}\pi| = 0$ (series resonance)

Solution. If the end of the line is open circuit, the voltage and current amplitude distributions along the line are given by $U_x = U_0 \cos 2\pi x/\lambda$ and $I_x = I_0 \sin 2\pi x/\lambda$, where x is the distance from the open end of the line, and U_0, I_0 are the amplitudes at corresponding loops. Hence, at the start of the line ($x = l$), $Z_{\text{in}} = |(U_0/I_0) \cot 2\pi l/\lambda|$. Since $U_0/I_0 = \varrho$, where ϱ is the characteristic impedance, we have $Z_{\text{in}} = |\varrho \cot 2\pi l/\lambda|$. The nature of the input impedance can be determined from the way it depends on the frequency: if it increases as the frequency increases (the wavelength diminishes), the impedance is inductive, if it falls with increase of the frequency it is capacitative. In case (1), the cot increases with increase of the argument (the second quadrant), and the impedance is inductive. In case (3) the cot diminishes with increase of the argument (third quadrant), and the impedance is capacitative. In case (2) the line is half a wave long and its beginning and end are occupied by current nodes, i.e. the current amplitude at the input is $I_{in} = 0$. This case is similar to parallel resonance in a lossless tuned circuit. In case (4) the line length is $5\lambda/4$ and there is a current loop at the input, so that, for a finite value of the input voltage amplitude U_{in}, we have $I_{in} = \infty$. This case is analogous to series resonance in a lossless tuned circuit.

491. $Z_{in} = \left| \varrho \tan \dfrac{2\pi x}{\lambda} \right| = \left| 216 \tan \dfrac{2\pi x}{6} \right|.$

The input impedance is inductive until the distance to the bridge is less than $\lambda/4$, i.e. $x < 1.5$ m. When $x = 1.5$ m, $Z_{in} = \infty$ (parallel resonance). When 1.5 m $< x < 3$ m, the input impedance is capacitative. When $x = 3$ m, $Z_{in} = 0$ (series resonance). When 3 m $< x < 4.5$ m the input impedance again becomes inductive, and so on.

Solution. Since the end of the line is short-circuited, the voltage and current amplitude distributions along the line are

$$U_x = U_0 \sin \frac{2\pi x}{\lambda}; \quad I_x = I_0 \cos \frac{2\pi x}{\lambda},$$

where U_0 and I_0 are the amplitudes at corresponding loops, x is the distance from the end of the line (bridge). And since $U_0/I_0 = \varrho$, we have

$$Z_{in} = \left| \varrho \tan \frac{2\pi x}{\lambda} \right|.$$

The nature of the loading is determined from the arguments described in the solution to Problem 490.

492. $Z_{in} = \left| 360 \cot \dfrac{2\pi(5 + 0.82)\text{ m}}{4\text{ m}} \right| \approx 1220 \text{ ohm},$

the impedance being inductive.

Solution. The capacity C across the end of the line can be replaced by a section of open-circuited line, the length l_{equ} of which is found from the condition that the capacitative impedance

$$X_C = |\varrho \cot l_{equ}/\lambda|.$$

Since the section of line has to replace a capacitative load, its length l_{equ} must be less than $\lambda/4$. On substituting the values from the conditions of the problem, we find that

$$l_{equ} = \frac{\lambda}{2\pi} \operatorname{arccot} \frac{X_C}{\varrho} = \frac{4}{2\pi} \operatorname{arccot} \frac{106}{360} \approx 0\cdot82 \text{ m.}$$

The problem now reduces to finding the input impedance of an open-circuit line of length $l + l_{equ} = 5\cdot82$ m (see Problem 424).

493. $Z_{in} = \left| 47 \cot \dfrac{2\pi(20 + 2\cdot44) \text{ m}}{11\cdot2 \text{ m}} \right| \approx 183$ ohm, the input impedance being capacitative.

Solution. As in the previous problem, we replace the inductance by a section of open-circuit line, the length of which is found from the condition that the inductive impedance $X_L = |\varrho \cot 2\pi l_{equ}/\lambda|$. We find from the conditions of the problem that $l_{equ} = 2\cdot44$ m. The problem now reduces to finding the input impedance of an open-circuit line.

494. (1) $R_{in} = \dfrac{\varrho^2}{R_1 l/2} \approx 260{,}000$ ohm.   (2) $R_{in} = \dfrac{R_1 l}{2} = 0\cdot5$ ohm.

Solution. (1) The line length is $5\lambda/4$, and when its end is short-circuited there must be current node at the input (since there is a current loop at the end). This case is therefore analogous to parallel resonance. But in the case of parallel resonance the equivalent impedance of the circuit is $Z_{equ} = X_{1,2}^2/R$, where $X_{1,2}$ is the reactive impedance of either circuit (since it is the same at resonance for both circuits). Further, since $X_2 = \omega L$, and $\omega = 1/\sqrt{LC}$, we have $Z_{equ} = L/CR = \varrho^2/R$, where $\varrho = \sqrt{L/C}$ is the "characteristic impedance" of the parallel circuit. Similarly, we have for parallel resonance in a line: $Z_{in} = \varrho^2/R_e$, where R_e is the "effective" resistance in the line, determined from the condition

$$R_0 I_0^2 = \int_0^l R_1 [i(x)]^2 dx = \tfrac{1}{2} R_1 l$$

(I_0 is the current amplitude at a loop). In other words, R_e is the resistance which, when connected at a current loop, produces the same loss as the actual resistance distributed along the line (since the current distribution is sinusoidal, the "effective resistance" is equal to half the actual). In the present case, therefore,

$$Z_{in} = \frac{\varrho^2}{R_1 l/2}.$$

(2) When the end is open-circuit, there is a current node at the input, which corresponds to series resonance. In the case of series resonance, the input impedance of the line is equal to the "effective" resistance (as in the case of series resonance in a tuned circuit), i.e.

$$R_{in} = \frac{R_1 l}{2}.$$

495. (1) $Z_{in} = \dfrac{\varrho^2}{r} = 2000$ ohm, (2) $Z_{in} = r = 80$ ohm.

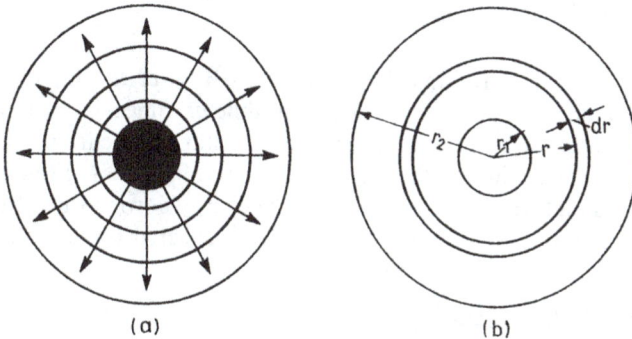

(a)　　　　　(b)

FIG. 200

496. $Z_{in} = 400$ ohm.

Solution. If the line is terminated by a resistance, equal to the characteristic impedance, no reflection occurs at the end of the line. Consequently, only a travelling wave is propagated in the line and the ratio of the voltage to current amplitudes is the same at all points of the line, and in particular, at the input, and is equal to ϱ.

497. The nature of the electric and magnetic fields in a concentric cable is shown in Fig. 200(a). The electric field of intensity E is

directed along the radii, the magnetic field of intensity H along the
tangents to circles. Here, $E = 2q/r = 2C_1u/r$ and $H = 2i/r$, where
C_1 is the capacity per unit length of the cable, r is the distance from
the axis of the cable, q is the charge per unit length, i the current in
the cable. By Poynting's theorem, the flux of energy traversing the
surface S in time dt is

$$dW_S = \frac{1}{4\pi} \int_S ([E \wedge H] \cdot dS)\, dt.$$

In the present case the energy flowing through the cross-section of
the cable in time dt is (Fig. 200(b)):

$$dW = \left[\frac{1}{4\pi} \int_S \frac{4C_1ui}{r^2}\, dS\right] dt = \left[\frac{1}{4\pi} \int_{r_1}^{r_2} \frac{4C_1ui}{r^2} \times 2\pi r\, dr\right] dt$$

$$= \left[2C_1ui \int_{r_1}^{r_2} \frac{dr}{r}\right] dt = 2C_1ui \ln\frac{r_2}{r_1}\, dt.$$

And since $C_1 = 1/(2 \ln r_2/r_1)$, we have $dW = ui\, dt$. But this ex-
presses the work done by the source in time dt. Since, in the case of
a travelling wave, the amplitudes of the voltage and current at any
section of the cable are the same as at the terminals of the source of
e.m.f., on integration over unit time the energy flowing through the
cross-section must be equal to the power delivered by the source.

498. (1) $I_x = I_0 \sin\dfrac{k\pi x}{l}$,

where I_0 is the current amplitude at the mid-point of the conductor
(at the current loop) and x is the distance from the input;

$$v_k = \frac{kc}{2l} = k \times 25 \times 10^6 \text{ c/s}, \quad \lambda_k = \frac{c}{n_k} = \frac{12}{k}\text{ m},$$

where $k = 1, 2, 3, \ldots$

(2) $I_x = I_0 \cos\dfrac{2k+1}{2}\dfrac{\pi x}{l}$,

where I_0 is the current amplitude at the earthing point (current loop) and x the distance from the earthing point.

$$\nu_k = \frac{2k + 1}{4} \frac{c}{l} = (2k + 1) \times 12{\cdot}5 \times 10^6 \, \text{c/s}; \quad \lambda_k = \frac{c}{n_k} = \frac{24}{2k + 1} \, \text{m},$$

where $k = 1, 2, 3, \ldots$.

499. $\lambda = 6$ mm.

500. $P = 20 \dfrac{\omega^2 l^2 I_e^2}{c^2} = 80\pi^2 \dfrac{l^2}{\lambda^2} I_e^2$, where I_e is the effective value of the current in the dipole.

501. $R_{\text{rad}} = 80$ ohm.

Solution. The field produced by each current element is proportional to the current in the element. If we assume that the fields from all the elements are in phase, the amplitude of the total field-strength will be proportional to $\int_0^l I(x)\, dx$, where l is the length of the dipole. Since the current distribution in the dipole is $I_x = I_0 \sin \pi x/l$, we have $\int_0^l I(x)\, dx = 2lI_0/\pi$. If the current distribution had been uniform, we should have obtained I_0. In other words, a half-wave dipole of length l produces the same field-strength as a dipole with a uniform distribution of current equal to the current at the loop of the half-wave dipole, and of length $l_1 = 2l/\pi$ (l_1 is called the "effective length" for the "effective height" of the half-wave dipole). Hence, to calculate the power radiated by a half-wave dipole, we only need to replace l in the previous answer by $2l/\pi$. We get

$$P = 80 \frac{4l^2}{\lambda^2} I_e^2 = 80 I_e^2 \left(\text{since } l = \frac{\lambda}{2}\right).$$

Consequently $R_{\text{rad}} = 80$ ohm.

We have performed the calculation on the assumption that the fields due to all the current elements are in phase. This is not quite true, however: the distances of the individual elements from the observation point are somewhat different, so that the phases of the fields are somewhat different. A more accurate calculation, taking this fact into account, gives the value $R_{\text{rad}} = 72$ ohm for the radiation resistance of a half-wave dipole.

502. $R_{rad} = 40$ ohm.

Solution. An earthed quarter-wave aerial produces above the ground the same field as would be produced by a half-wave aerial (of twice the length) if the ground were absent, in other words, the quarter-wave aerial produces only the "upper half" of the half produced by the corresponding half-wave aerial, i.e. radiates half the power. The radiation resistance of the earthed quarter-wave aerial is therefore half that of the half-wave aerial, i.e. $R_{rad} = 40$ ohm.

503. $R'_{rad} = 140$ ohm.

Solution. Since the dipoles are close together, their fields are in phase at any given point, and they produce twice the field produced by each separately. They therefore radiate together four times the power, and each radiates twice the power that it would in the absence of the other. Each dipole thus has twice the radiation resistance that it would have in the absence of the other.

504. The full-wave dipole can be regarded as two half-wave dipoles mounted in line. The fields of these dipoles generally speaking have a phase-shift at any given point. The power radiated by them will consequently be less than that radiated by two dipoles mounted parallel and close to one another (as considered in the previous problem). The radiation resistance of the full-wave aerial is therefore less than the sum of the radiation resistance of the two dipoles of the previous problem. On the other hand, in the case of two separate, i.e. remote dipoles, it can be assumed that they will radiate independently, whereas for a full-wave aerial the fields are in phase over the greater part of space, i.e. they add up. Hence the radiated power, and thus the radiation resistance of a full-wave dipole is greater than the sum of the radiated powers, and hence of the radiation resistances, of two separate half-wave dipoles.

505. $E_e \approx 2 \cdot 2$ mV/m.

Solution. The effective electric field-strength of a half-wave dipole in the equatorial plane (see Problem 500) is

$$E_e = 30 \frac{2\pi}{\lambda} \frac{2l}{\pi} \frac{I_e}{r} = 60 \frac{I_e}{r},$$

where I_e is the effective current at the dipole loop. Since, on the other hand, $I_e = \sqrt{P/R_{rad}}$, where R_{rad} is the radiation resistance, we have $E_e = (60/r) \sqrt{P/R_{rad}}$. For a half-wave dipole,

$$R_{rad} = 72 \text{ ohm} \quad \text{and} \quad E_e \approx \frac{7\sqrt{P}}{r} \text{ Vm}^{-1}.$$

506. $P \approx \dfrac{60}{8\pi^2} \dfrac{P}{R_{rad}r^2} \dfrac{\pi D^2}{4} \approx 8 \times 10^{-6} \text{ W},$

where R_{rad} is the radiation resistance of the dipole, equal to 72 ohm.

507. *Solution.* The e.m.f. produced by the incident wave in the receiving dipole can develop in each element dx of the dipole the maximum power $dP = I_e(x)E_e dx$, where I_e is the effective current in the element and E_e the effective field-strength of the incident wave. In the entire half-wave dipole the incident wave can develop the maximum power

$$P = \int_0^l I_{0e} \sin \frac{\pi x}{l} E_e dx = \frac{2l}{2} I_{0e} E_e,$$

where I_{0e} is the effective current in the loop. Consequently, the receiving dipole can be regarded as a source of e.m.f. $\mathscr{E}_e = 2lE_e/\pi$ (so that $2l/\pi$ is called the "effective length" of the half-wave dipole) with an internal resistance R_l. This internal resistance can never be less than the radiation resistance R_{rad} (which it possesses in addition to ohmic resistance). The dipole will deliver maximum power to the receiver if the receiver input impedance $R_{in} = R_{rad}$. The total resistance of the circuit is now $2R_{rad}$, and the total power liberated in the circuit is $P = \mathscr{E}_e^2/2R_{rad}$.

When the external and internal resistances are equal, half this power will go into the receiver, so that the maximum power which the receiver can obtain is

$$P_{max} = \frac{\mathscr{E}_e^2}{4R_{rad}} = \frac{E_e^2(2l/\pi)^2}{4R_{rad}} = \frac{E_e^2 l^2}{\pi^2 R_{rad}}.$$

508. In the plane through the axis of the oscillator, Fig. 201 (a); in the equatorial plane at right angles to the axis, Fig. 201 (b).

509. As the length of the dipole increases the phase difference between the fields arriving at a given point from different elements of the dipole will become substantial (Fig. 202 (a)). This phase difference is the greater, the greater the angle φ. Hence the amplitude of the dipole field will no longer be equal, at large angles φ, to the sum of the amplitudes from the individual elements, but will be less than this. This means that the polar diagram in the plane through the dipole axis flattens out (Fig. 202(b)). In the plane perpendicular to the axis, the diagram remains circular as before.

510. (1) Figure 203(a), (2) Figure 203(b).

511. Figure 204(a).

Solution. Since the phase difference between corresponding points of the dipoles is π, the individual fields will be in phase in directions

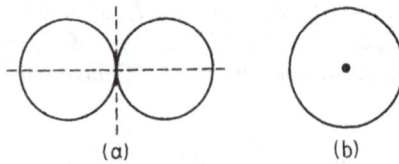

(a)   (b)

Fig. 201

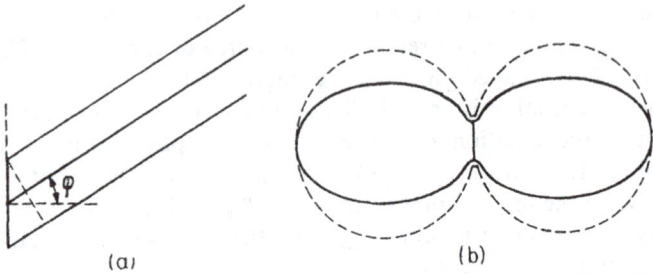

(a)   (b)

Fig. 202

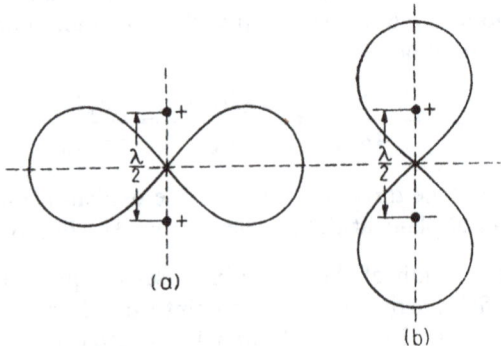

(a)   (b)

Fig. 203

in which the path difference is $d = \frac{1}{2}\lambda$. But since $d = \lambda \sin \varphi$ (Fig. 204(b)), these directions correspond to an angle $\varphi = 30°$ with the perpendicular to the line joining the dipoles. The field-strength is a maximum in all four directions satisfying this condition. There will be no radiation in the direction of the line joining the dipoles.

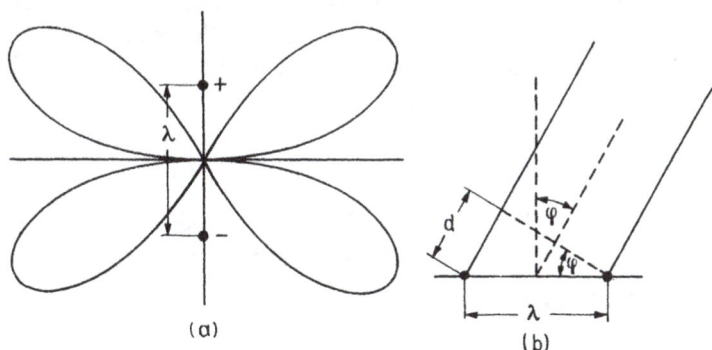

(a)   (b)

Fig. 204

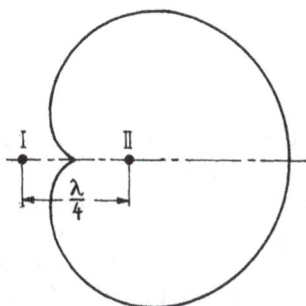

Fig. 205

512. Figure 205.

Solution. The second dipole, at a distance $\lambda/4$ from the first and fed by current lagging $\frac{1}{2}\pi$ behind the first, eliminates the radiation in the direction of the line joining the second to the first dipole (since the phase shift between the fields of the two dipoles is π in this direction). Conversely, in the direction from the first to the second dipole the path difference compensates the phase shift, the two fields are in phase and the radiation has a maximum in this direction. If the second dipole is not fed directly by current, but has a length chosen so that the current of the first dipole produces in it a current shifted $\frac{1}{2}\pi$ in phase relative to the first, it acts as described above. Such "passive" dipoles are called reflectors.

513. Figure 206(a).

Solution. The main lobe maximum corresponds to the direction in which the fields of all the dipoles are in phase. If we represent the fields of the dipoles as identical vectors, the main maximum direction corresponds to the disposition of the vectors shown in

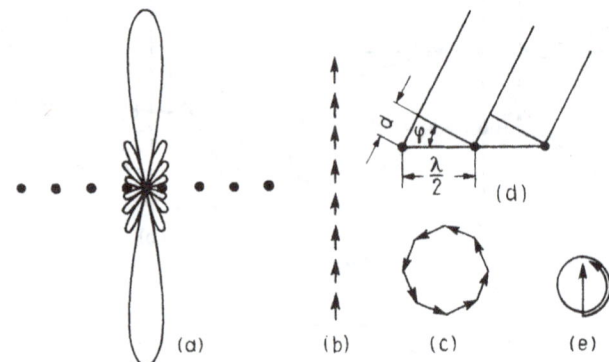

FIG. 206

Fig. 206(b). In any other direction there is a phase difference between the fields of the individual dipoles, corresponding to rotations of the vectors through a certain angle relative to one another. When the vectors form a closed polygon (Fig. 206(c)), the resultant field is zero. This occurs the first time when the vectors are turned through $\pi/4$ relative to one another and form an octagon. The corresponding path difference is $d = \lambda/8$ (Fig. 206(d)), i.e. $\sin\varphi = \frac{1}{4}$ or $\varphi \approx 14°30'$. The two minima will be at this angle in both directions from the main maximum, i.e. the total angle of the main lobe is $2\varphi = 29°$. The maximum of the first side lobe is obtained when the vectors have performed one and a half revolutions; their resultant then has a maximum again. To estimate the size of this maximum we replace the step line formed by the vectors with an arc of a circle. Since one and a half revolutions of this arc must have a length equal to the sum of the lengths of all the vectors, the diameter of the circle (Fig. 206(e)) must be $3\pi/2$ times less than the length of the straight line of Fig. 206(b). The amplitude of the first side lobe maximum is therefore $3\pi/2 \approx 5$ times less than the amplitude of the main maximum, or 25 times less in power. With a large number of dipoles this ratio is independent of the number of dipoles.

514. (1) The upper part of Fig. 203(b) in the solution of Problem 510; (2) the upper part of Fig. 204(a) in the solution of Problem 511. The directions of the maxima of the diagram are given by

$$n \sin \varphi_{max} = (2k + 1) \frac{\lambda}{4};$$

the directions of the minima are given by

$$n \sin \varphi_{min} = k \frac{\lambda}{2},$$

where φ is the angle above the horizontal, k is an integer.

Solution. Since "image charges" of opposite sign must be taken in the method of mirror images, the "image dipole" below the earth's surface has to be regarded as oscillating in opposite phase to the dipole above the earth. The present cases therefore correspond to the images in Figs. 203(b) and 204(a).

515. Figure 207.

FIG. 207

516. The directions of the maxima of the diagram are given by

$$n \sin \varphi_{max} = \frac{k}{2},$$

and the minima by

$$n \sin \varphi_{min} = \frac{2k + 1}{4},$$

where φ is the angle above the horizontal, k is an integer.

Solution. In the case of a vertical dipole, given opposite signs for the "image charges", the direction of the current in the "image dipole" is the same as in the dipole above the earth. Hence both dipoles are in phase, so that the directions of the maxima and minima are interchanged compared with the case of a horizontal dipole (see the answer to Problem 514).

517. For the frame,

$$E_e = \frac{30\omega^2 nd^2 I_e}{c^2 r} \approx 1 \times 10^{-4} \, \mathrm{Vm}^{-1}.$$

For a Hertz oscillator of length d, fed by a current I_e,

$$E_e = \frac{30\omega dI_e}{cr} \approx 1.25 \times 10^{-3} \, \mathrm{Vm}^{-1},$$

i.e. the field of the single wire is greater than that of the frame as a whole.

Solution. Each individual wire of the frame produces a field like the Hertz oscillator, but the currents in opposite sides of the frame are in opposite directions, so that the fields produced by them are in opposite directions. As a result of this, the resultant field in the plane of the frame (Fig. 208) is given by

$$E = \frac{30\omega ndI_0}{cr} \sin \omega \left(t - \frac{r_1}{c} \right) - \frac{30\omega ndI_0}{cr} \sin \omega \left(t - \frac{r_2}{c} \right)$$

$$= \frac{30\omega ndI_0}{cr} \, 2 \sin \omega \, \frac{r_1 - r_2}{c} \sin \omega \left(t - \frac{r_1 + r_2}{2c} \right).$$

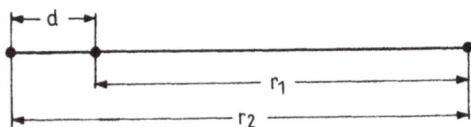

FIG. 208

Since $r_1 - r_2 = d$, $\omega d \ll c$, then $2 \sin \dfrac{\omega d}{2c} \approx \dfrac{\omega d}{c}$ and

$$E = \frac{30\omega^2 nd^2 I_0}{c^2 r} \sin \omega \left(t - \frac{r_{\mathrm{av}}}{c} \right),$$

$$E_e = \frac{30\omega^2 nd^2 I_e}{c^2 r}.$$

The frame therefore produces the same field as would be produced by a Hertz oscillator of length $l_{eff} = \omega nd^2/c = 2\pi nd^2/\lambda$. This quantity is therefore called the "effective height" of the frame. The field of the frame is less than the field produced by all the wires forming one side of the frame, in the ratio $2\pi d/\lambda$ (due to the fact that the fields from opposite sides of the frame have almost opposite phase).

518. Figure 209.

519. $\mathscr{E} = E \dfrac{\omega nd^2}{c} \approx 2\,\mu\text{V}$.

Solution. Since the electric field of the incident wave produces e.m.f.'s in opposite directions in opposite sides of the frame, similar

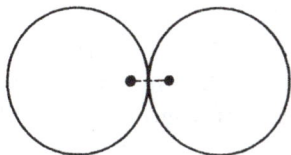

FIG. 209

relationships to those for the field produced by the frame in Problem 517 hold for the field of the incident wave. The same expression $l_{eff} = \omega nd^2/c$ therefore holds for the effective height of the receiving as for the transmitting frame (in the present case $l_{eff} = 4$ cm). The e.m.f. induced in the frame is $\mathscr{E} = El_{eff}$. The relationship for the e.m.f. in the Hertz doublet is the same as in the previous problem.

520. $v = \dfrac{c}{\sqrt{1 - \dfrac{4\pi N}{\omega^2}\dfrac{e^2}{m}}}$

(c is the velocity of light *in vacuo*, e and m are the charge and mass of an electron).

Solution. The displacement x of a free electron under the action of the electric field $E_0 \sin \omega t$ is given by

$$m \frac{d^2x}{dt^2} = E_0 e \sin \omega t,$$

whence $x = -(E_0 e/m\omega^2) \sin \omega t$. The magnitude of the electric polarisation vector $P = Nex = -(E_0 Ne^2/m\omega^2) \sin \omega t$, whilst the electric induction vector

$$D = E_0 \sin \omega t + 4\pi P = E_0(1 - 4\pi Ne^2/m\omega^2) \sin \omega t.$$

The dielectric constant of the ionosphere $\varepsilon = D/(E_0 \sin \omega t) = 1 - 4\pi Ne^2/m\omega^2$. Since the velocity of propagation of a harmonic wave ("phase velocity") $v = c/\sqrt{\varepsilon}$, on substituting the expression found for ε, we obtain the answer.

521. $\lambda_{min} = c \cos \varphi \sqrt{\dfrac{\pi m}{Ne^2}} \approx 23 \text{ m}$

(c is the velocity of light *in vacuo*, e and m are the charge and mass of the electron).

Solution. The condition for total internal reflection of a wave propagated in a medium with refractive index n_1 and incident at an angle φ to the boundary of a medium with refractive index n_2 is $\sin \varphi > n_2/n_1$.

In the case of a wave travelling from the earth to the boundary of the ionosphere, $n_1 \approx 1$, whilst the refractive index of the ionosphere (see the previous solution) is $n_2 = \sqrt{1 - 4\pi Ne^2/\omega^2 m}$.

For the limiting case, when total internal reflection from the boundary of the ionosphere is still possible,

$$\sin \varphi = \sqrt{1 - 4\pi Ne^2/\omega_{max}^2 m},$$

whence the expression given above follows for the shortest wavelength:

$$\lambda_{min} = \frac{2\pi c}{\omega_{max}}.$$

Made in Great Britain

Made in the USA
Monee, IL
04 February 2025